English
Key Stage 2

Set A
Reading Booklet

This booklet contains:

Deserts

Dishes Around the World

Kidnapped

CGP

EHPP24

2

Contents

DESERTS

What is a desert?

A desert is defined as a place that receives less than 250 mm of rainfall a year — to put this in context, in London 600 mm of rain falls on average each year.

Despite what many people think, desert landscapes are not just seas of sand. Deserts, which cover approximately one third of the Earth's land surface, can be anything from rocky plains to vast expanses of ice to dramatic mountainous regions. As you might imagine, the world's deserts also suffer extreme temperatures, with air temperatures in the hottest deserts reaching more than 56 °C during the daytime.

Antarctica

That being said, not all of the deserts of the world are hot. The continent of Antarctica at the Earth's southern pole is the coldest and iciest area in the world. 50 mm of precipitation does fall each year in the Antarctic desert, but it only falls as snow or ice crystals, not rain. The temperature rarely creeps above 0 °C and can plummet as low as −89 °C! This desert is extensive, covering an area nearly double the size of Australia.

Very few animals and plants have the ability to survive in such a hostile environment. In fact, Antarctica's larger inhabitants spend most of their time at sea. Penguins are covered in closely packed oily feathers that repel water, and they also benefit from a layer of fat that provides them with warmth. Seals have a fat-filled layer of spongy tissue called blubber that insulates them from the extreme temperatures. One species, the Weddell seal, which lives further south than any other mammal, dives for fish through holes in the ice.

Atacama Desert

Apart from the poles, the driest place on Earth is the Atacama Desert in Chile, South America. The Atacama is a barren, rocky desert that is bounded on one side by the Pacific Ocean. It has an average annual rainfall of less than 15 mm each year, although fog rolls in from the ocean to bring some life-saving moisture. The desert covers 105,000 square kilometres and temperatures range from 35 °C by day to −4 °C by night.

Cactuses and hardy grasses are the only plants that can survive in this harsh climate. A few remarkable mammals also live here: the viscacha (similar in

A South American grey fox.

appearance to a rabbit), the South American grey fox and Darwin's leaf-eared mouse. With scarcely any places to conceal themselves, these small mammals often have large ears to help them detect both predators and prey. As an added bonus, this feature also helps these animals to lose body heat more efficiently.

Arabian Desert

The greatest continuous area of sand in the world is found in the famous Empty Quarter which forms part of the Arabian Desert. The Arabian Desert is located in Western Asia and extends across an area of over 2,300,000 square kilometres. It has an average of 100 mm of rainfall a year, and temperatures can soar to over 50 °C in its hottest regions. The vast quantity of sand contained in the desert is whirled around by winds into striking hilly shapes called sand dunes.

Animals that have adapted to survive in the Arabian Desert include gazelles, oryx, sand cats and spiny-tailed lizards. Some lizards have long toes that prevent them from sinking into the sand and fat tails that serve as an energy store. The Arabian oryx is small, so it can shelter under little trees, and it is able to walk considerable distances to obtain food and water in this barren landscape.

Dishes Around the World

It stands to reason that a country's local dishes will contain ingredients that are in plentiful supply in that area of the world. The crops that are grown, the animals that thrive on those crops, and the herbs and spices added to dishes will be governed by a country's climate and geography. However, there are other factors that influence the traditional foods that are eaten in different places: religion and historical events play their part too. Let's explore how and why dishes vary around the world.

Geography

Coastlines, climate, mountains and soil quality all have a major impact on a country's native foods. Sometimes there are large enough variations in geography even within single countries to result in an exciting range of regional delicacies.

Italy is a southern European country that offers a variety of tempting dishes made from local produce. The north and south of the country are very different geographically: the north is colder and more mountainous, with rich soil suited to wheat, maize and rice, while the south, which has rocky ground, is hot and dry — perfect for olives and lemons.

Olives growing on a tree

India is an immense country in southern Asia with an extremely varied climate: cold northern peaks and tropical, flatter areas in the south. In northern India, the main crop grown is wheat, which is ground down to make bread. In the balmy south, the principal crop is rice but millet is also grown there.

Japan is a chain of over 6000 islands in the Pacific Ocean. Nowhere in Japan is farther than 90 miles from the sea; this proximity to the ocean results in a cuisine dominated by appetising seafood dishes. This, paired with their rice production, leads to the traditional dish, sushi (right). It is made by rolling fish or vegetables in sticky rice, then wrapping this in sheets of dried seaweed.

History

A country's history can also have a marked effect on its national eating habits. In the past, Italy has been invaded and occupied by several other countries from across Europe — all of which have had a profound influence on Italian food. For example, during their rule in the 1500s, the Spanish introduced the tomato to Italy — a fruit now regarded as a staple in Italian cooking. The migration of Greeks into Italy brought with it Greek culture and the introduction of a type of flat bread which over the years developed into the crowd-pleasing pizza we recognise today.

Influences from abroad do not always originate from invasion and migration. Thousands of years ago, China began growing rice. Historians believe rice was then introduced to Japan, where farmers cut flat strips of land (terraces) into the mountainside. Today, Japan is the tenth largest rice producer in the world, while China is the largest.

Rice terraces

Religion

As well as geography and history, religious beliefs can also determine local eating habits. Some faiths forbid the consumption of particular types of meat, or specify how food should be prepared. One country where religious belief has influenced cuisine is India. The majority of the population in India practise Hinduism, a religion which teaches nonviolence, and, as such, Hindus usually follow a vegetarian diet. It is therefore not surprising that Indian cooking contains a wealth of vegetarian dishes. This is not to say that Indian cuisine is limited, however — it is famous for its enticing variety of delicious spices.

Identifying a nation's traditional cuisine presents a difficult yet fascinating task; preferences for certain foods can change over time, and one country can embrace a wide range of specialities drawn from different regions. We can use the United Kingdom as an example. Fish and chips might be thought of as one of the nation's favourite traditional dishes, but its position has recently been challenged by the rising popularity of other dishes such as chicken tikka masala — a type of curry heavily influenced by Indian culture.

Dishes that originate in one country can become popular in another as people travel around the world and share their culture. You don't need vast amounts of wealth to experience the special dishes of different places, as local delicacies are often great value. So next time you're travelling, test your taste buds and try something new!

Kidnapped

Kidnapped tells the story of 17-year-old David, who has recently lost his parents. He finds out he has a wealthy uncle, Ebenezer, and goes to stay with him. However, his uncle seems to dislike David. One day, Ebenezer takes David to visit one of the ships he does business with. David goes aboard, where he is suddenly knocked unconscious. The following extract begins when David wakes...

I came to myself in darkness, in great pain, bound hand and foot, and deafened by many unfamiliar noises. There sounded in my ears a roaring of water as of a huge mill-dam, the thrashing of heavy sprays, the thundering of the sails, and the shrill cries of seamen. The whole world now heaved giddily up, and now rushed giddily downward; and so sick and hurt was I in body, and my mind so much confounded, that it took me a long while, chasing my thoughts up and down, and ever stunned again by a fresh stab of pain, to realise that I must be lying somewhere bound in the belly of that unlucky ship, and that the wind must have strengthened to a gale. With the clear perception of my plight, there fell upon me a blackness of despair, a horror of remorse at my own folly, and a passion of anger at my uncle, that once more bereft me of my senses.

When I returned again to life, the same uproar, the same confused and violent movements, shook and deafened me; and presently, to my other pains and distresses, there was added the sickness of an unused landsman on the sea. In that time of my adventurous youth, I suffered many hardships; but none that was so crushing to my mind and body, or lit by so few hopes, as these first hours aboard the brig*.

I heard a gun fire, and supposed the storm had proved too strong for us, and we were firing signals of distress. The thought of deliverance, even by death in the deep sea, was welcome to me. Yet it was no such matter; but (as I was afterwards told) a common habit of the captain's, which I here set down to show that even the worst man may have his kindlier side. We were then passing, it appeared, within some miles of Dysart, where the brig was built, and where old Mrs. Hoseason, the captain's mother, had come some years before to live; and whether outward or inward bound, the Covenant was never suffered to go by that place by day, without a gun fired and colours* shown.

   *brig = ship   *colours = ship's flag

I had no measure of time; day and night were alike in that ill-smelling cavern of the ship's bowels where I lay; and the misery of my situation drew out the hours to double. How long, therefore, I lay waiting to hear the ship split upon some rock, or to feel her reel head foremost into the depths of the sea, I have not the means of computation. But sleep at length stole from me the consciousness of sorrow.

I was awakened by the light of a hand-lantern shining in my face. A small man of about thirty, with green eyes and a tangle of fair hair, stood looking down at me.

"Well," said he, "how goes it?"

I answered by a sob; and my visitor then felt my pulse and temples, and set himself to wash and dress the wound upon my scalp.

An extract from
Kidnapped
by Robert Louis Stephenson

English

Key Stage 2

Set A
Reading
Answer Booklet

1 hour

First name	
Middle name	
Last name	
School	

Date of birth	Day		Month		Year	

How to Answer the Questions

This booklet contains questions for you to answer in different ways. There are three main types of question:

• **short-answer questions**

  You'll get one or two lines to write your answer on, so just write a word, a short phrase or a single sentence.

• **long-answer questions**

  You'll be given several lines to write your answer on. You should use full sentences and explain your answer in more detail, giving reasons for your opinion or using quotations from the reading text.

• **other types of answer**

  For some questions, you do not have to write anything. Instead, you might have to tick the correct box, circle the right answer or draw lines to match up words. Read the questions carefully and they'll tell you what to do.

Marks

The maximum number of marks for each question is written underneath a box at the side of the page.

Don't do anything until you are told to.

Start on page 3. Work through the booklet until you are told to stop. Read one text and answer the questions on it before moving on to the next text. Use your reading booklet whenever you need to.

When a question mentions a particular page of the reading booklet, look at that page to help you write your answer.

You will have 1 hour to read the texts in the booklet and answer the questions.

SECTION 1

These questions are about *Deserts*

1.   Choose the best word or group of words to fit the sentences below, and circle your choice.

     a)   A desert is classified as having an annual rainfall of less than

         150 mm.   250 mm.   200 mm.   600 mm.

         1 mark

     b)   According to the text, people generally think of deserts as

         rocky and mountainous.   dry and empty.   cold and icy.   vast and sandy.

         1 mark

     c)   The temperature range in the Antarctic is between 0 °C and

         98 °C.   −89 °C.   89 °C.   −4 °C.

         1 mark

     d)   This desert is home to the world's southernmost mammal, a type of

         penguin.   fox.   oryx.   seal.

         1 mark

Deserts

2.   *Very few animals and plants have the ability to survive in such a hostile environment.*

What does the word *hostile* mean in the sentence above?

....

1 mark

3.   How does the Pacific Ocean help life survive in the Atacama Desert?

....

....

1 mark

4.   *...the viscacha (similar in appearance to a rabbit)...*

Explain how comparing the viscacha to a rabbit helps the reader understand what a viscacha looks like.

....

....

....

1 mark

5. *...into striking hilly shapes called sand dunes.*

   What does the word *striking* tell you about the sand dunes in the Arabian Desert?

   ....

   ....

   1 mark

6. Give **one** difference between Antarctica and the Arabian Desert.

   ....

   1 mark

7. Read each sentence and tick **one** box to show whether it is **true** or **false**.

	True	False
The Atacama Desert borders the Atlantic Ocean.	☐	☐
Cactuses are the only plants that can survive in the Atacama Desert.	☐	☐
Sand dunes are formed by the wind.	☐	☐
The biggest area of sand in the world is the Atacama Desert.	☐	☐

   1 mark

8.   Animals have adapted in many ways in order to survive in deserts.

      Give **two** different ways they have adapted, using information from the text.

      1. ....

      ....

      2. ....

      ....

2 marks

9. a) Suggest **one** of the main ideas of the text.

      ....

1 mark

    b) **Find** and **copy** a phrase which supports your choice.

      ....

1 mark

SECTION 2

> **These questions are about** *Dishes Around the World*

10. Tick **two** things that are affected by a country's climate and geography, according to the text.

Tick **two** boxes.

its historical events ☐

its religion ☐

its crops ☐

its spices ☐

1 mark

11. *Let's explore how and why dishes vary around the world.*

How does starting the sentence above with *Let's explore* make the reader feel about reading the rest of the text?

....

....

1 mark

12. Name **two** crops grown in Italy and **two different** crops grown in India according to the text.

Italy: ....

....

India: ....

....

2 marks

13.   Name a country where the crops grown differ from region to region.

....

1 mark

14.   *...this proximity to the ocean results in a cuisine dominated by appetising seafood dishes.*

Which of the following words has a similar meaning to *proximity*?

Tick **one** box.

preference   ☐

location   ☐

closeness   ☐

distance   ☐

1 mark

15.   Which of these is a traditional Japanese dish?

Tick **one** box.

sticky rice   ☐

sushi   ☐

pizza   ☐

dried seaweed   ☐

1 mark

16. How might Italian cooking be different today if the Greeks had not migrated into Italy?

....

1 mark

17. Look at the section titled *History*.

   Tick the statement which best describes the main idea of the whole section.

   Tick **one** box.

   Migration affects a country's cuisine. ☐

   Cuisine can be influenced by other countries. ☐

   Invasions affect a country's cuisine. ☐

   China and Japan have similar cuisines. ☐

1 mark

18. Compare the cuisines of Japan and India.

   Use evidence from the text to support your answer.

....

....

....

....

2 marks

19. Read each sentence and tick **one** box to show whether it is a **fact** or an **opinion**.

	Fact	Opinion
Lemons are grown in southern Italy.	☐	☐
Japan is made up of thousands of islands.	☐	☐
The tomato is the most important ingredient in Italian cuisine.	☐	☐
The spices added to Indian dishes make them delicious.	☐	☐

1 mark

20. Name **two** popular dishes eaten in the UK.

1. ....

2. ....

1 mark

21. The word *wealth* is used in two different ways in the text.

For each context, explain the meaning of the word.

Context	Meaning
...a **wealth** of vegetarian dishes.	....
You don't need vast amounts of **wealth**...	....

2 marks

22.	How does this text make the reader feel about trying different dishes from around the world?

	Explain your answer using examples from the text.

SECTION 3

These questions are about *Kidnapped*

23.   What is the purpose of the first paragraph on page 9?

        ....

1 mar

24.   Who is the story being told by?

        ....

1 mar

25.   Look at the paragraph that begins *I came to myself in darkness...*
        Find and **copy three** words that show it is noisy aboard the ship.

        1. ....

        2. ....

        3. ....

1 mar

26.   David begins to understand his situation on page 9. What does he realise?

        ....

        ....

1 mar

12

27.   Read the paragraph that begins *I came to myself in darkness...*
      How does this paragraph make the reader feel?

      ....

      1 mark

28.   How do you know that David has fainted?

      ....

      ....

      1 mark

29.   **Find** and **copy** a word or phrase from page 10 that suggests that David had
      a difficult time when he was young.

      ....

      1 mark

30.   *The thought of deliverance, even by death in the deep sea, was*
      welcome to me.

      Which word has a similar meaning to *deliverance*?

                        Tick **one** box.

      release   ☐

      company   ☐

      kindness   ☐

      ransom   ☐

      1 mark

---

31. Look at the paragraph that begins *I heard a gun fire...*
Explain why the guns are being fired.

....

....

1 mar

32. a) Which of the following best describes David?

Tick **one** box.

He is honest and just. ☐

He is cruel and cunning. ☐

He tries to see the best in people. ☐

He is contented. ☐

1 mar

b) **Find** and **copy** a sentence or phrase which supports your answer.

....

....

1 mar

33. *I had no measure of time; day and night were alike in that ill-smelling cavern...*

Explain what the phrase *day and night were alike* suggests about the part of the ship where David is being kept.

....

1 mark

34. Look at the paragraph that begins *I had no measure of time...*

What does David think is going to happen next?

....

1 mark

35. Explain how David's situation improves at the end of the extract.

....

....

....

....

2 marks

36. What do you think **happens next** in the story?

Explain your answer using information from the text.

....

....

....

....

....

....

....

3 marks

END OF TEST

15

[Blank Page]

English
Key Stage 2

Set B
Reading Booklet

This booklet contains:

All About Mice

An Amsterdam Adventure

Tales from Outer Space

Contents

All About Mice

The thought of a mouse and its long, swishing tail makes some people want to scream, but believe it or not, mice make great, affectionate pets. These nocturnal creatures (awake in the early evening and at night) have an average lifespan of between 1.5 and 3 years, and they are omnivores, with a diet of both meat and plants. Before deciding if a pet mouse is the right choice for you, you should get to know the facts about caring for these pocket-sized pets.

Housing

Every mouse needs somewhere to live. It might seem obvious but your mouse's cage will be where it spends most of its time, so it needs to be large and secure. It must also have an adequate air flow as mice have sensitive lungs and frequently develop breathing problems. Ensure that the cage is positioned in a peaceful location, as mice doze through the day and are easily startled.

Mice are also fond of digging and tunnelling, so their cages should be filled with a few centimetres of loose material to allow them to burrow to their heart's content. One of the safest, most straightforward options is shredded newspaper, but be aware that some ink can be toxic. Avoid using wood shavings, as they are frequently dusty which can damage a mouse's lungs.

Warm and dry bedding material is a must, and ripped-up kitchen roll is ideal for this purpose. Steer clear of thick bedding such as cotton wool as it can get caught around your mouse's legs, with dangerous consequences.

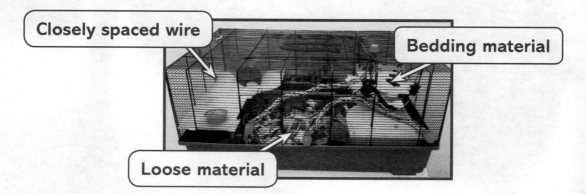

Closely spaced wire

Bedding material

Loose material

Mice ought to be fed a 'complete food' (which contains all the nourishment necessary for your mouse) and fresh drinking water should be constantly available. Complete food can be purchased in blocks, each of which has the same texture, flavour and nourishment. The advantage of this is that you won't be anxious that your mouse will only eat its favourite parts of its food. However, food made up of a variety of parts like seeds and nuts is more appealing for your mouse, as wild mice spend a large part of their day searching for different types of food.

Occasional treats won't be an issue, but they should form less than a tenth of your mouse's regular diet. Chocolate, crisps and some other human treats can be poisonous to mice, so be wary of this danger. Mice love a range of fruit and vegetables, which can be given in limited amounts on a daily basis. Carrots, broccoli, bananas and blueberries will all be much appreciated by your resident rodent, as will foods like wholemeal bread, boiled eggs, mealworms, and cooked brown rice.

However, there are several foods mice cannot digest. Garlic, onions and rhubarb are among these unsuitable items, and, although mice like the taste of fruits, they should not be offered citrus fruits, grapes, raisins or apple seeds. Remember to wash food before placing it in your mouse's cage, and remove uneaten food the following day to prevent it from rotting.

When introducing a new type of food, start by only giving tiny amounts (smaller than the size of your mouse's ear), in case your mouse is allergic to it.

Toys and Exercise

Mice spend a large amount of time in their cage, so providing a variety of different toys will keep them busy. They are prey animals and in the wild they often hide to escape from predators; to recreate this sense of security in your mouse's cage, cardboard tubes and boxes make excellent toys. The majority of mice are enthusiastic climbers, so hanging toys are popular too. Furthermore, since a mouse's teeth grow constantly, chew toys are beneficial for keeping them short.

Exercise is essential for keeping your mouse fit and healthy. Running wheels are a crucial item in any cage, but they must be selected carefully. They should be solid, as wheels formed from wire bars are painful and can damage your mouse's feet. Be sure to purchase a wheel of a large enough size that your mouse's back is not overly arched when it is running.

A 'flying saucer' wheel.

Recently, spinning disc or 'flying saucer' wheels have increased in popularity as they allow mice to run in a more natural manner.

Danger Signs

If you think anything is wrong with your pet, contact a vet immediately. Be alert for danger signs such as a dramatic weight loss or changes in your mouse's fur (for example, becoming rough or spiky). If your mouse breathes noisily, or begins to cough and wheeze, you should also call the vet. Altered behaviour, such as becoming noticeably less active, is another warning sign that your mouse may have a health problem.

Choosing the right pet is really important. Hopefully this information will enable you to decide whether you are up to the task of looking after a mouse.

An Amsterdam Adventure

Sophie is on her way from England to Amsterdam, a city in the Netherlands, for a short holiday with her mum.

4th March

Day one of the holiday! Unfortunately, things didn't start particularly well. When our coach pulled up at the port, I was full of anticipation as I had never travelled by ferry before. That rapidly changed once we were underway... On the rare occasion that I tried to walk anywhere I was tossed sideways as the ship violently lurched, making my stomach churn. I attempted to sit motionless and gaze out of the window, but the constant tilting of the horizon just made me feel even more queasy. To my relief, we were soon back on the coach trundling in the direction of Amsterdam.

By the time we arrived at our hotel in central Amsterdam it was mid-afternoon, and Mum was flustered and frustrated. A rumoured car accident had brought traffic to a virtual standstill, so we had spent what felt like hours snaking our way slowly through the city. When we eventually got off the coach, we decided to stroll out into the city, and Mum visibly began to relax.

After a short while, we stumbled across the Basilica of St. Nicholas — a magnificent Catholic church. I never imagined *that it would be so awe-inspiring! We were like tiny ants next to its pointed towers. The windows were dazzling; they were made up of hundreds of vibrant shards of glass. Colours danced on the stone walls as the sunlight streamed through them. I could have gazed at them for hours.*

5th March

After breakfast, we hired some bikes and headed to the Vondelpark — a sprawling expanse of parkland towards the south of the city. Lakes were scattered throughout the park, each one surrounded by spindly reeds and skeletal trees still recovering from winter. We stopped beside the largest lake to take some pictures as a family of ducks paddled their way across its rippling surface. The wind began to nip at us so we reluctantly rode off.

Meandering along a side street, we heard the din of the traditional market long before we could see it. We turned a corner near the canal and I was taken aback. The wide square was alive: traders laughed and argued, food steamed and filled the air with mouth-watering smells and the cobbles were bustling with people. I had to constantly dive out of the paths of determined shoppers. One stall displayed numerous pieces of delicate jewellery. Mum bought me a silver bracelet with round lilac gemstones nestled in it. Another sold sweetly fragrant tulips (the Netherlands' most famous flower) in an unbelievable range of colours. A third was serving a selection of local delicacies. I tried a dish called bitternballen — crisp round shells packed with beef. The first one scalded my tongue, but after they had cooled they were delicious.

Next, we visited a museum dedicated to the painter, Vincent Van Gogh. It was crammed full of people. We spent most of our time waiting behind dawdling groups, craning our necks in a vain attempt to glimpse the art. Whenever we managed to squeeze to the front, we could feel the impatience of the people behind us. We eventually cut our losses and left because we wanted to fit in a canal boat tour before dusk.

The canal tour was a relaxing and thoroughly enjoyable way to travel on the water! The ride was smooth and I sank back gratefully into my chair. Headphones were available for listening to facts as we cruised past points of interest, but after a while I stopped listening, preoccupied with taking pictures of the towering, narrow buildings lining the water. The boat dropped us off near a quaint restaurant where we ended the day with a quiet dinner.

Tomorrow, it's back to the coach for our return to England. Travelling around Amsterdam has been delightful and I desperately wish we could have extended our trip. Maybe we could visit again next year...

Tales from Outer Space

An interview via videophone with astronaut **Madeleine Ryan**.

Madeleine Ryan is both a scientist and an astronaut. Originally from Florida in the USA, she has spent the past two months living and working on the World Space Station (WSS), an artificial satellite orbiting the Earth.

Madeleine, how did you come to be aboard the WSS?

Astronomy was my original line of work. You could say I study the world beyond Earth: the wonders of stars, galaxies, quasars and globular clusters. This fascination with space motivated me to train as an astronaut. When I tell interviewers that, although I have been a qualified astronaut for five years, this is my first time in space, they are puzzled. The majority of an astronaut's work is done on the ground: intense training and mission preparation, alongside conducting research in your area of expertise. My extensive knowledge of our red neighbour, Mars, led to my inclusion on this mission.

Why is a Mars specialist needed on the WSS?

Remote-controlled machines have recently been successfully deployed to explore Mars, so currently there's significant interest in sending a manned craft to orbit the planet —

perhaps one day to even land there. As an astronomer, I study conditions on Mars and collaborate with the other scientists on board to determine whether this could be achievable. Views of Mars from the ground are distorted by the gases making up the Earth's atmosphere. Taking readings whilst in orbit greatly increases the accuracy of our results.

Madeleine is investigating whether man could ever land on Mars.

Is there a typical day for you on the WSS?

Life aboard the WSS is regimented — meticulously planned by our colleagues back on the ground. Our schedules dictate when we wake, eat, work and sleep. Scientists even plan our menus down to the last morsel to make sure that our bodies receive all the necessary nutrients. Exercise is an important element of our daily routine, as being in space is tough on the human body. The WSS is equipped with a treadmill, with a special harness so we don't float away when we're using it!

What influenced you to follow this career path?

The overwhelming influence came from my grandfather, a keen amateur astronomer who gifted me my first telescope when I was eight. I would spend countless hours at my bedroom window, gazing up at the stars. My mother would regularly complain to my father: "That child has always got her head in the clouds!" Growing up in Florida, the launch site of American space shuttles since 1981, also inspired me. I still get shivers down my spine when I recall hearing the tense countdown to take-off, and then the colossal roar of the rocket boosters.

What would you say to youngsters who dream of being astronauts?

I would say that you should dream about space, but don't be a daydreamer in real life — you have to be determined, and physical fitness is vital. But, with a bit of perseverance, you can certainly succeed. It's inspiring to share the space station with a host of similarly motivated, talented colleagues. Being up here now, I can see sprawling continents and vast oceans down on Earth, and the never-ending blackness of space. A view like this is worth every painstaking second of effort!

A shuttle launch at Cape Canaveral, Florida.

English

Key Stage 2

Set B
Reading
Answer Booklet

1 hour

First name	
Middle name	
Last name	
School	

Date of birth	**Day**		**Month**		**Year**	

How to Answer the Questions

This booklet contains questions for you to answer in different ways. There are three main types of question:

- **short-answer questions**

    You'll get one or two lines to write your answer on, so just write a word, a short phrase or a single sentence.

- **long-answer questions**

    You'll be given several lines to write your answer on. You should use full sentences and explain your answer in more detail, giving reasons for your opinion or using quotations from the reading text.

- **other types of answer**

    For some questions, you do not have to write anything. Instead, you might have to tick the correct box, circle the right answer or draw lines to match up words. Read the questions carefully and they'll tell you what to do.

Marks

The maximum number of marks for each question is written underneath a box at the side of the page.

Don't do anything until you are told to.

Start on page 3. Work through the booklet until you are told to stop. Read one text and answer the questions on it before moving on to the next text. Use your reading booklet whenever you need to.

When a question mentions a particular page of the reading booklet, look at that page to help you write your answer.

You will have 1 hour to read the texts in the booklet and answer the questions.

SECTION 1

These questions are about *All About Mice*

1. Read each sentence and tick **one** box to show whether it is a **fact** or an **opinion**.

	Fact	Opinion
Mice tend to live for between 1.5 and 3 years.	☐	☐
It is great to have a mouse for a pet.	☐	☐
Before getting a mouse, you should learn the facts.	☐	☐
Mice eat both plants and animals.	☐	☐

☐
1 mark

2. Give **one** reason why a mouse's cage should be placed somewhere quiet.

    ....

    ....

    ☐
    1 mark

3. Why is it dangerous to put wood shavings in a mouse's cage?

    ....

    ☐
    1 mark

3

4.   **Find** and **copy** a phrase from the text which suggests that mice drink water often.

      ....

1 mark

5.   *Complete food can be purchased in blocks, each of which has the same texture, flavour and nourishment.*

      What does the word *nourishment* mean in this sentence?

      ....

1 mark

6.   Explain why mice might not grow properly if they are fed a diet of mixed seeds and nuts instead of blocks.

      ....

      ....

1 mark

7.   Tick **two** foods that mice should not eat.

      mealworms ☐   crisps ☐

      grapes ☐   bananas ☐

      carrots ☐

1 mark

8. Why should you only give a mouse a small amount of a new type of food?

....

1 mark

9. **Find** and **copy** a word that shows that an exercise wheel is a necessary item in a mouse cage.

....

1 mark

10. What does the increased popularity of flying saucer wheels suggest about current mice owners? Support your answer with information from the text.

....

....

1 mark

11. Name **two** things other than an exercise wheel that should be put in a mouse cage and explain why each one is important.

1. ....

....

2. ....

....

2 marks

12. Explain **two** differences you might notice between a healthy mouse and a sick mouse.

....

....

....

....

....

2 mark

13. How does the summary at the end of the text link back to the introduction?

....

....

1 mark

14. *Hopefully this information will enable you to decide whether you are up to the task of looking after a mouse.*

What does the phrase *up to the task* suggest about taking care of mice?

....

1 mark

15. What is the overall message of the text?

Tick **one** box.

That it's a good idea for everyone to own a mouse ☐

That people should be well informed before buying a mouse ☐

That mice are brilliant pets ☐

That mice get lots of health problems ☐

1 mark

SECTION 2

> These questions are about *An Amsterdam Adventure*

16. Why was Sophie thankful to get back onto the coach after the ferry journey?

   ....

   1 mark

17. Why was Sophie's mum *flustered and frustrated* on the first day of their trip?

   ....

   ....

   1 mark

18. *We were like tiny ants next to its pointed towers.*

   What does the phrase *like tiny ants* tell you about the towers of the Basilica of St. Nicholas?

   ....

   1 mark

19. *...they were made up of hundreds of vibrant shards of glass.*

   Which of the following is closest in meaning to the word *vibrant*?

   Tick **one** box.

   brightly coloured ☐

   delicate ☐

   tiny ☐

   pale ☐

   1 mark

7

20.   What does the word *sprawling* tell you about the Vondelpark?

....

....

1 mark

21.   Write down **three** things that you are told about the market square.

1. ....

2. ....

3. ....

1 mark

22.   *...the cobbles were bustling with people. I had to constantly dive out of the paths of determined shoppers.*

Circle the option which best describes the shoppers in the market.

Tick **one** box.

angry

focused

hesitant

observant

1 mark

23.   What food did Sophie eat at the market?

....

1 mark

24. What do you think Sophie's opinion of the market was?

Explain your answer using evidence from the text.

....

....

....

....

....

....

....

3 marks

25. Which of these is the best description of the Van Gogh museum?

Tick **one** box.

A large, impressive building ☐

A popular tourist destination ☐

Sophie's favourite place in Amsterdam ☐

The Netherlands' biggest museum ☐

1 mark

26.   *...craning our necks in a vain attempt to glimpse the art.*

What does the word *vain* mean in the sentence above?

....

1 mark

27.   How did the canal tour compare to the ferry crossing?

....

....

1 mark

28.   What do you think Sophie and her mum would do differently if they visited Amsterdam again? Use evidence from the text to support your answer.

....

....

....

....

....

2 marks

29.   Put these events in the order they happen in the text.

The first one has been done for you.

Sophie tries local food.   ☐

Sophie receives a gift.   ☐

Sophie admires stained glass windows.   1

Sophie goes to a lake.   ☐

Sophie visits a museum.   ☐

SECTION 3

> **These questions are about *Tales from Outer Space***

30. What technology was used for this interview?

   ....

1 mark

31. *... World Space Station (WSS), an artificial satellite orbiting the Earth.*

   Which is closest in meaning to the word *artificial* in the sentence above?

   Circle the correct answer.

   Tick **one** box.

   fake ☐

   revolving ☐

   man-made ☐

   natural ☐

1 mark

32. What was Madeleine Ryan's first profession?

   ....

1 mark

33. How long has Madeleine been an astronaut for?

   ....

1 mark

34. Why was Madeleine needed on the WSS?

....

1 mark

35. Why is it easier to study Mars from the WSS than it is from Earth?

Explain your answer using information from the text.

....

....

....

1 mark

36. Read each sentence and tick **one** box to show whether it is **true** or **false**.

	True	False
An astronaut is trained mostly in space.	☐	☐
The WSS is going to land on Mars next year.	☐	☐
You can see the Earth from the WSS.	☐	☐
Astronauts choose their own food.	☐	☐

1 mark

37. *Life aboard the WSS is regimented...*

What does the word *regimented* mean in the sentence above?

....

1 mark

38. What event was the main factor in Madeleine's choice of career?

....

1 mark

39. In which part of the USA did Madeleine watch space missions taking off as a child?

....

1 mark

40. *I still get shivers down my spine when I recall hearing the tense countdown to take-off, and then the colossal roar of the rocket boosters.*

How do the words *shivers*, *tense* and *colossal roar* make the reader feel about rockets taking off?

....

....

1 mark

41. Read each sentence and tick **one** box to show whether it is a **fact** or an **opinion**.

	Fact	Opinion
Madeleine has spent two months on the WSS.	☐	☐
Robots have been sent to Mars.	☐	☐
Daydreaming won't make you successful.	☐	☐
Being an astronaut is worth the intense training.	☐	☐

1 mark

42. a) Which of these four options best summarises the main idea of the text?

Exploring Mars is an important mission. ☐

Being an astronaut is a great job. ☐

Becoming an astronaut is hard work. ☐

Exercising in space is vital. ☐

☐
1 mark

b) Explain your choice using information from the text.

....

....

....

☐
1 mark

43. How does the final paragraph make the reader feel about the life of an astronaut? Use information from the text to support your answer.

....

....

....

....

☐
2 marks

END OF TEST

[Blank Page]

Total marks

English
Key Stage 2

Set A
Grammar, Punctuation and Spelling

Paper 1 — Questions
45 minutes

First name	
Middle name	
Last name	
School	

Date of birth	Day		Month		Year	

[Blank Page]

Instructions

This booklet tests your **grammar**, **vocabulary** and **punctuation**. The test has different question types, which you will need to answer in different ways. Each question has a space for you to give your answer. This will show you the type of answer to give:

Multiple-choice answers: you can answer these questions without writing any words. You might have to tick a box, circle a word or draw lines between different words. Read the instructions for each question carefully, as they will tell you what to do.

Short answers: these questions have a line or a box for your answer. This shows that you need to write something. It could be a word, a short phrase or a sentence.

Marks

There is a mark box next to each question. It tells you the maximum number of marks for that question.

Do not start until your teacher tells you to. Once you have started the test, work through the booklet until you are told to stop.

You will have 45 minutes to answer all the questions.

1. Read the sentence below.
   Insert **commas** so that the sentence is punctuated correctly.

   All of the pupils like English, and most of them also enjoy maths

   art science and sport.

2. Draw a line to match each sentence with the most likely final
   punctuation mark. You can only use each punctuation mark **once**.

   Sentence   **Punctuation**

   | Why are you crying | | ? |

   | We should go to the park | | ! |

   | How amazing that is | | . |

3. Read the sentence below. Insert a **comma** in the correct place.

Panting and out of breath Phil crossed the finish line.

4. Read the sentences below.
    Tick the sentence that's written in **Standard English**.

Tick **one** box.

She were disappointed with the final score. ☐

I done my chores quickly to have more free time. ☐

We were talking about going to Majorca on holiday. ☐

Robbie would of preferred pizza for dinner. ☐

5. Read the sentence below.
   Write what Helene adds as a list of bullet points below.
   Make sure you use correct punctuation.

   When making a cup of coffee, Helene adds boiling water, a splash of milk and two sugar cubes.

   When Helene makes coffee, she adds:

   - _____

   - _____

   - _____

1 mar

6. Read the sentence below and circle the word or words that make it a **question**.

   They aren't going to be late, are they?

1 mar

7. Read the sentences below.
   Circle all the words that need **capital letters**.

   "do you know how to get to the train station?" asked trevor.

   "I think i'm lost."

1 mar

8. Tick the **pair of verbs** which completes the sentence correctly.

Albert _____ too old to play badminton, but thirty years ago

he _____ a top player.

Tick **one** box.

was	is	☐
was	was	☐
is	was	☐
is	is	☐

1 mark

9. Circle the **subject** and underline the **object** in the sentence below.

My sister posted a heavy parcel.

1 mark

10. Look at the table below.
For each answer, write an appropriate question.

One has already been done for you.

Question	Answer
What do you like to eat at the cinema?	Popcorn.
	There are twelve.
	She sings.

11. Read the sentences below. In each box, write the **contracted form** of the words that are underlined.

The classroom <u>has not</u> been tidied this week because <u>it is</u> nearly Christmas.

After the holidays, <u>we will</u> tidy everything up.

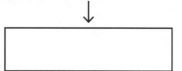

12. Read the sentence below. Circle the two **conjunctions**.

Samantha said she wanted pasta or a sandwich to eat for lunch,

but she didn't mind which one.

13. Look at the table below. Complete the table by adding suitable **antonyms**.

Word	Antonym
brave	
energetic	

14. Read the sentences below. Tick the **two** sentences which are **commands**.

Tick **two** boxes.

A wok is a large, wide saucepan. ☐

Cut up the vegetables into chunks. ☐

Hard vegetables like carrots take longer to cook. ☐

Serve with some soy sauce. ☐

1 mar

15. Complete the sentences below by replacing the underlined word or words with the correct **possessive pronoun**.

That book is owned by <u>me</u>. That book is _____.

This bag belongs to <u>you</u>. This bag is _____.

Those gloves belong to <u>my sister</u>. Those gloves are _____.

1 mar

16. Read the sentences below. Replace the underlined words in each sentence with an appropriate **pronoun**. Write the pronoun in the box.

Stephanie's mum decorated the cake nicely.
↓

[ ]

The cake was covered with gold stars.
↓

[ ]

17. Put a tick in each row of the table below to show how the **modal verb** affects the **meaning** of the sentence.

Sentence	Modal verb shows **possibility**	Modal verb shows **certainty**
Mairi might come and visit in a few weeks.		
Josh will play better than that.		
Helen and Keith may be coming for dinner.		
I shall arrive at seven o'clock in the morning.		

18. Read the sentence below.
    Tick **one** box to show the position of the **adverb**.

    Louise liked reading books, so she often went to the library in town.

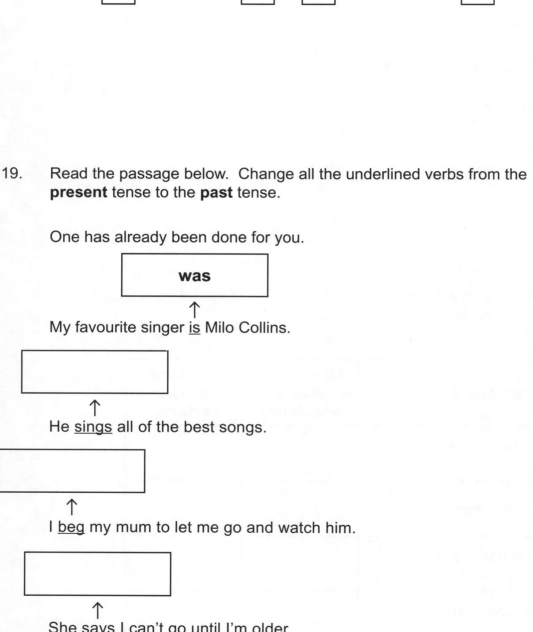

19. Read the passage below. Change all the underlined verbs from the
    present tense to the **past** tense.

    One has already been done for you.

was

    My favourite singer <u>is</u> Milo Collins.

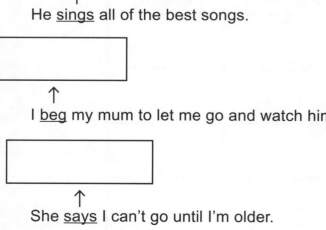

    He <u>sings</u> all of the best songs.

    I <u>beg</u> my mum to let me go and watch him.

    She <u>says</u> I can't go until I'm older.

20. The sentence below is missing a **colon**.
Tick **one** box to show where the colon should go.

We got there just in time the show was about to begin.

21. Explain how the different **prefixes** in the two sentences below change their meanings.

The votes were <u>miscounted</u>.

This means that the votes _____

_____

The votes were <u>recounted</u>.

This means that the votes _____

_____

13

22. In the sentence below, Elliott is allowed to go out because he has finished his homework.
Read the sentence, then write the correct **verb** in the space.

Elliott _____ finished his homework, so he went

out to see his friends.

23. Read the sentence below. Tick **one** box to show the sentence's **function**.

What a great idea that was

Tick **one** box.

a statement	☐
an exclamation	☐
a question	☐
a command	☐

English

Key Stage 2

Total marks

Set A
Grammar, Punctuation and Spelling

Paper 2 — Spelling

First name	
Middle name	
Last name	
School	

Date of birth	Day		Month		Year	

CGP

Spelling Test

1. I am worried that my jeans will ....

2. The spare .... are in that drawer.

3. If I stretch my arms, I can .... the ceiling.

4. The bus is .... minutes late.

5. He was .... the best basketball player in the school.

6. Olivia's new rabbit is ....

7. Kevin .... some oranges at the market.

8. She thought the man looked ....

9. I tried to .... them to come swimming.

10. The girls packed the .... ready for the field trip.

11. There was .... that the man was guilty.

12. I .... learning German to French.

13. At the start of her .... , the Queen threw

a big party.

14. She is a .... of the company.

15. Raj's new, orange door caused much ....

16. A warm coat is .... in this terrible weather.

17. Jamie lives on a tropical ....

18. I will .... the award on Tuesday.

19. By the evening, everyone was tired and ....

20. My friend is an .... footballer.

END OF TEST

[Blank Page]

24. Read the sentence below. Put a tick by the word which is a **preposition**.

After dinner, Will declared loudly that he was full.

Tick **one** box.

After ☐

that ☐

he ☐

full ☐

1 mark

25. Read the sentence below and circle all the **determiners**.

There isn't much chocolate left — we should go to the shop.

1 mark

26. Read the sentence below.
    Rewrite the sentence as **direct speech**. Make sure you use correct punctuation.

    Anthony said that the new museum is full of interesting exhibits.

    Anthony said, _____

    _____

27. a) Give an explanation of the word **synonym**.

    _____

    _____

    b) Give one word that is a **synonym** of <u>angry</u>.

    _____

28. Read the sentences below.
Underline the **subordinate clause** in each sentence.

Although I like cars, I didn't enjoy visiting the transport museum.

Despite being tired, Sonia tried her best in the running race.

Callie watched television while Allan did his homework.

1 mark

29. Put a tick in each row of the table below to show whether the words in bold are **adjectives** or **adverbs**.

Sentence	Adjective	Adverb
He walked down the **narrow** street.		
Make sure you stay **close**.		
Andrew hit the ball **hard**.		
I gave her a **challenging** task.		

1 mark

30. Read the sentences below.
Tick the sentence that uses **dashes** correctly.

Tick **one** box.

The hare chased — Harry my best friend — across the park. ☐

The hare — chased Harry — my best friend across the park. ☐

The hare chased — Harry my best friend across — the park. ☐

The hare chased Harry — my best friend — across the park. ☐

1 mark

31. Circle **two suffixes** which can be added to the word below to create new words.

music

-al   -ment   -ful   -ian   -ise

1 mark

32. Rewrite the sentence below so that it is in the **passive voice**. Use the words from the sentence, and add extra words where appropriate.

Vicky repaired the car.

_____

33. Read the sentence below and circle the **relative clause**.

The biscuits which are in the tin have gone soft.

34. Read the sentences below.
    Tick the sentence which uses the **past progressive**.

    Tick **one** box.

    Tom had a great time at the concert. ☐

    Alys stroked the cat gently. ☐

    Ian and Leah were dancing together. ☐

    Fern forgot about the meeting. ☐

1 mark

35. Put a letter in each box to show which **word class** the words belong to.

    | verb A | noun B | determiner C | adverb D |

    Saeed has every sticker in the album, but soon we will have them all too.
    ↑   ↑   ↑   ↑
    ☐   ☐   ☐   ☐

1 mark

36. Read the sentence below. Tick the **relative pronoun** that completes the sentence correctly.

We didn't know the person _____ knocked loudly at our door.

Tick **one** box.

whom ☐

whose ☐

who ☐

which ☐

1 mark

37. Look at the table below. Add your own words before and after the noun to make your own **noun phrase**.

One has already been done for you.

Noun	Noun phrase
the cushion	the fluffy cushion on my bed
the house	

1 mark

38. Read the two sentences below. Explain how the meaning changes when the **comma** is added.

Urvi had an odd collection of chocolate mice and jam.

Urvi had an odd collection of chocolate, mice and jam.

_____

_____

39. Read the sentences below.
Tick the sentence which uses a **dash** correctly.

Tick **one** box.

Ben wanted to — drive he knew the route. ☐

Ben wanted to drive — he knew the route. ☐

Ben wanted to drive he — knew the route. ☐

Ben wanted to drive he knew — the route. ☐

40. Rewrite the sentence below so it starts with the **adverbial**. Only use the words from the sentence, and make sure you use correct punctuation.

We said goodbye to Gran before lunch.

_____

_____

1 mark

41. Read the sentences below. Underline the **main clause** in each sentence.

Once we'd found the missing piece, we finally finished the jigsaw.

Toby went home after we'd eaten our picnic.

Before you go swimming, don't forget to feed the rabbits.

He tried to fix the tyre that the dog had bitten.

1 mark

42. Read the sentences below.
Tick the sentence which uses the **hyphen** correctly.

Tick **one** box.

The doctor saw forty nine year-olds in one day. ☐

The doctor saw forty-nine year olds in one day. ☐

The doctor saw forty nine-year olds in one day. ☐

The doctor saw forty nine-year-olds in one day. ☐

1 mar

43. Complete the sentence below by ticking the option that correctly introduces the **subordinate clause**.

Phoebe really liked Paulo, _____ she thought his brother was silly.

Tick **one** box.

although ☐

unless ☐

despite ☐

regarding ☐

1 mar

44. Read the sentence below.
Which **word class** does the word '**run**' belong to?

During her **run**, Alexis listened to music.

Tick **one** box.

adverb ☐

verb ☐

noun ☐

preposition ☐

1 mark

45. Look at the **word family** below.
What does the root '**port**' mean in this word family?

porter   transport   portable

Tick **one** box.

boat ☐

carry ☐

send ☐

drink ☐

1 mark

46. Read the sentence below. Tick the verb that completes the sentence so that it uses the **subjunctive form**.

If I _____ too hot, I would open the window.

Tick **one** box.

was ☐

were ☐

am ☐

get ☐

1 mark

47. Read the sentences below.
Tick the sentence which uses **semi-colons** correctly.

Tick **one** box.

Christina packed; a tube of suncream, a large, frilly hat and a pair of sunglasses. ☐

Christina packed a tube of suncream a large, frilly hat; and a pair of sunglasses. ☐

Christina packed a tube of suncream, a large; frilly hat, and a pair of sunglasses. ☐

Christina packed a tube of suncream; a large, frilly hat; and a pair of sunglasses. ☐

1 mark

48. Put a tick in each row of the table below to show whether the word in bold is a **co-ordinating conjunction** or **subordinating conjunction**.

Sentence	Co-ordinating conjunction	Subordinating conjunction
Moeen goes swimming **and** diving.		
I will only go **if** the weather is nice.		
You can call me tonight, **or** you can call me tomorrow night.		

1 mark

49. Put a tick in each row of the table below to show whether the words in bold are a **noun phrase** or a **subordinate clause**.

Sentence	Noun phrase	Subordinate clause
My dog is good at chasing rabbits **because she's so quick**.		
The grumpy woman plodded along the street.		
Everyone was jealous of **Claire's new running shoes**.		
Eugene listened to the radio **while his wife had a nap**.		

1 mark

END OF TEST

[Blank Page]

English
Key Stage 2

Set B
Grammar, Punctuation and Spelling

Paper 1 — Questions
45 minutes

Total marks

First name	
Middle name	
Last name	
School	

Date of birth	Day		Month		Year	

[Blank Page]

Instructions

This booklet tests your **grammar**, **vocabulary** and **punctuation**. The test has different question types, which you will need to answer in different ways. Each question has a space for you to give your answer. This will show you the type of answer to give:

Multiple-choice answers: you can answer these questions without writing any words. You might have to tick a box, circle a word or draw lines between different words. Read the instructions for each question carefully, as they will tell you what to do.

Short answers: these questions have a line or a box for your answer. This shows that you need to write something. It could be a word, a short phrase or a sentence.

Marks

There is a mark box next to each question. It tells you the maximum number of marks for that question.

Do not start until your teacher tells you to. Once you have started the test, work through the booklet until you are told to stop.

You will have 45 minutes to answer all the questions.

1. Read the sentences below. Put a tick in each row of the table to show whether the word is a **verb** or an **adjective**.

James likes <u>fast</u> cars; he loves to <u>attend</u> racing events.

He also likes to <u>cycle</u> to work on his <u>shiny</u> bike.

Word	Verb	Adjective
fast		
attend		
cycle		
shiny		

1 mark

2. Tick **one** box to show where the **full stop** should go to separate the sentences.

Running is a great sport Ian often goes running in York with his sister.

1 mark

3. The sentence below is missing an **exclamation mark**.
    Tick **one** box to show where the exclamation mark should go.

    "Come back here" shouted Tom as Zak marched away from him.

1 mark

4. Read the sentences below.
    Circle all the words that need **capital letters**.

    last week, harriet had to go to hospital. the doctor said that

    her leg would heal in time for her summer holiday in august.

1 mark

5. Draw lines to make new words by matching each **prefix** to the correct word.

Prefix	Word
ir	appropriate
in	marine
sub	vision
tele	interested
un	regular

6. Read the sentences below.
Tick the sentence that needs a **question mark** at the end.

Tick **one** box.

You should ask Hadia what she thought of the new film ☐

Benjamin asked if I had seen the new film ☐

You haven't seen it already, have you ☐

The girls wanted to know when we were going to see it ☐

7.   Read the sentence below and circle all the **adjectives**.

Ellie, my youngest sister, reluctantly climbed the rusty ladder.

8.   Read the sentences below.
Tick the sentence that uses **inverted commas** correctly.

Tick **one** box.

"Put your pencils" away, said the teacher.   ☐

Put your pencils away," said the teacher.   ☐

"Put your pencils away," said the teacher.   ☐

"Put your pencils away said" the teacher.   ☐

7

9. Write a **question** on the line below that begins with the word '**what**'.

What _____

10. Read the sentence below.
Circle the two words that show the **tense** in the sentence.

Owen's grandfather worked as a butcher until he was seventy years old.

11. Read the passage below. What does the word '**any**' refer to?

There were lots of cakes, including chocolate brownies, at the party.
I don't think any were as good as my brother's biscuits though.

Tick **one** box.

cakes ☐

chocolate brownies ☐

party ☐

biscuits ☐

12. Read the sentence below and circle the **conjunctions**.

Lesley bought a dress and a large hat but she couldn't find

a bag before the shops closed, so she ordered one online

once she got home.

13. Read the sentences below.
Tick the **preposition** that completes **both** sentences.

I put the box of books _____ the bed.

_____ Tuesday, we went to the cinema.

Tick **one** box.

on ☐

in ☐

under ☐

above ☐

1 mar

14. Write the **contracted forms** of the words on the left, using **apostrophes** in the correct places.

he is _____

could not _____

I am _____

will not _____

1 mar

15. Read the sentence below.
Circle all of the **pronouns**.

When we got to the dining hall, Lucy and Pete invited us

to sit with them.

1 mark

16. Tick **one** box to show where the **hyphen** should go in this sentence.

When I was six years old, we made a non stop journey to Tokyo.

1 mark

17. Complete the sentences below by filling in each gap with an **adjective** formed from the verb in the box.

break

Irene thinks that the radio is _____ because it keeps switching

itself off. It's disappointing because listening to music was _____.

18. Tick **one** word which is a **synonym** of 'majestic'.

Tick **one** box.

large ☐

gentle ☐

grand ☐

sweet ☐

19. Read the sentence below and underline the **possessive pronoun**.

He thought Lorraine's cake was far less burnt than mine.

1 mark

20. Read the sentence below. Replace the underlined word with a **more formal** word. Write the word in the box.

Iain's teacher was <u>chuffed</u> with his results.

1 mark

21. Tick the sentence below that has been punctuated correctly.

Tick **one** box.

The thief, who was very crafty, stole money, rings, and a painting. ☐

The thief, who was very crafty, stole money, rings and a painting. ☐

The thief who was very crafty stole money, rings and a painting. ☐

The thief, who was very crafty, stole money rings and a painting. ☐

1 ma

22. Look at the table below. Complete the table by adding suitable **antonyms**.

Word	Antonym
weak	
peaceful	

1 mar

English

Key Stage 2

Set B

Grammar, Punctuation and Spelling

Paper 2 — Spelling

First name	
Middle name	
Last name	
School	

Date of birth	Day		Month		Year	

Spelling Test

1. I .... seaweed for the first time today.

2. My teacher asked me to .... my pets.

3. My writing is always .... when I rush.

4. He walked .... along the beach.

5. Eric wrote the date of the party on his ....

6. One day, Jemma will own her own ....

7. Sandy will .... Eddie to the wedding.

8. My mum is the .... at this restaurant.

9. Sanjay .... forgot to send the letter.

10. I .... that you go to the zoo during the holidays.

11. Stan is a .... member of the rowing team.

12. The sweets are filled with a sugary ....

13. Which .... of the game did you play?

14. Sandra's .... hurt after she drank lots of milk.

15. It's amazing what you can .... if you put your mind to it.

16. Megan's football team is top of the ....

17. There was a .... between two rugby players.

18. It is hard to see in this .... daylight.

19. Mark is .... of the fact that time is running out.

20. She has learnt how to sail a ....

END OF TEST

[Blank Page]

23. a) Read the sentence below. Write the **name** of the punctuation marks on either side of the words <u>long before anyone else</u>.

I got up early — long before anyone else — so that I would arrive on time.

_____

b) Write the name of a **different** punctuation mark that could be correctly used in its place.

_____

24. Look at the table below. Put a tick in each row to show whether the clause in **bold** is a **main** clause or a **subordinate** clause.

Sentence	Main clause	Subordinate clause
There was a rainbow **even though it wasn't raining**		
Since there was nothing to do, the boys were very bored.		
Before the tide came in, **we packed the picnic away**.		

25. Read the sentence below. Put **V** in the box under the **verb**, **S** in the box under the **subject** and **O** in the box under the **object**.

Ashleigh caught a fish.

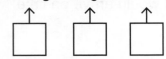

1 mar

26. Read the sentence below and circle the **relative pronoun**.

I went to see the concert that was advertised in the newspaper.

1 mar

27. Rewrite the sentence below so it starts with the **adverbial**. Only use the words from the sentence, and make sure you use correct punctuation.

Sam was content and relaxed before the performance.

_____

_____

1 mark

28. Three members of the Smith family are talking about their holiday. Read the sentence below and add **commas** to make the meaning clearer.

While they helped Sarah Thomas and Joe Smith chatted

about their holiday.

1 mark

29. Read the sentences below.
Tick the sentence that uses **dashes** correctly.

Tick **one** box.

The weather was — bad awful actually so — I stayed indoors. ☐

The weather was bad — awful actually — so I stayed indoors. ☐

The weather — was bad awful actually so I — stayed indoors. ☐

The weather was bad awful — actually so I stayed — indoors. ☐

1 mar

30. Complete the sentence below by filling in the gaps with the **present progressive** form of the verbs in the boxes.

I _____ a board game at the moment, and unfortunately

my sister _____ , but that's all about to change.

1 mar

31.   Read the sentences below. Underline the **subordinate clause** in each sentence.

Before we could park, we drove around for twenty minutes.

I don't like car racing because the cars are too loud.

Nilam went skating after she took the dog for a walk.

When I grow up, I want to be a vet.

1 mark

32.   Read the sentences below.
Circle all of the **determiners**.

I have a glass of orange juice every morning before school.

My Grandma says the vitamins in it will keep me healthy.

1 mark

33. Read the sentence below.
Tick the word that is an **adverb**.

The children were very quiet while they were waiting.

Tick **one** box.

very ☐

quiet ☐

while ☐

waiting ☐

34. Tick the box below the part of the sentence that is a **relative clause**.

That castle | which was built by the Normans | is still standing | today.

35. Look at the table below. Put a tick in each row to show whether each sentence is a **statement** or a **command**.

Sentence	Statement	Command
You can use the hose to wash the car.		
When you have finished, tidy away the hose and sponges.		
If the car is really clean, Dad will give you extra pocket money.		

1 mark

36. Read the sentence below.
What is '**the excited puppy**' an example of?

Damia decided to bring **the excited puppy** into the house.

Tick **one** box.

a conjunction ☐

a relative clause ☐

an adverbial phrase ☐

a noun phrase ☐

1 mark

37.   Write your own sentence using the word '**show**' as a **verb**.
      Use correct punctuation in your sentence.

      _____

      1 ma

      Write your own sentence using the word '**show**' as a **noun**.
      Use correct punctuation in your sentence.

      _____

      1 ma

38.   Read the sentence below and write down the name of a **punctuation mark** that
      could replace '**, but heard**'.

      Sarah stopped and listened**, but heard** nothing but a humming sound.

      _____

      1 ma

39. Read the sentences in the table. Put a tick in each row to show whether the words in bold are the **subject** or **object** of the sentence.

Sentence	Subject	Object
I love **you**.		
The new computer is great.		
His favourite sport is **tennis**.		
My grandmother welcomed the guests.		

1 mark

40. a) Circle the **two words** in the sentence below that should have an **apostrophe**.

Its a shame — the shops have sold out of walking boots in

Andrews size.

b) Pick one of the words that you have circled. Explain why it needs an apostrophe.

Word chosen _____

_____

_____

1 mark

41. Read the sentence below.
Underline the longest **noun phrase** there is in the sentence.

The oak tree at the bottom of the garden has been there for two hundred years.

1 ma

42. The word 'until' can be either a **subordinating conjunction** or a **preposition**.
Put a tick in each row to show how '**until**' is used in each sentence.

Sentence	Preposition	Subordinating conjunction
Count sheep **until** you fall asleep.		
Until he apologises, I'm not talking to him.		
The shop is closed **until** 8 am.		

1 ma

24

43. Read the sentences below.
Tick the event that is **most likely** to happen.

Tick **one** box.

David might pass his exams. ☐

I will bake some biscuits. ☐

Tina can come with us. ☐

We could go to the cinema. ☐

1 mark

44. Write down a word that belongs to the same **word family** as the words below.

trilogy   triathlon   tripod

_____

1 mark

45.   Read the sentences below.
        Tick the sentence that uses the **perfect form.**

                                                                    Tick **one** box.

        Jamal had sent his friend a letter, but he did not expect a reply.   ☐

        I once went to a magic show and was invited to take part on stage.   ☐

        My cat used to be aggressive, but now she is much calmer.   ☐

        Sara loved flowers, and she had a large garden.   ☐

1 ma

46.   Rewrite the sentence below so that it is in the **passive voice**. Use the words
        from the sentence, and add extra words where appropriate.

        Julian ate the big hamburger.

        _____

1 ma

47. Read the information in the box below. Write one sentence that lists all this information. Make sure you use correct punctuation.

> **Shopping list**
> washing-up liquid
> sponges
> a present (for Michael)
> potatoes

_____

_____

1 mark

48. Tick the option below that completes the sentence in the **subjunctive form**.

If I _____ you, I would tell Benjamin the truth.

Tick **one** box.

am ☐

were ☐

could be ☐

was ☐

1 mark

END OF TEST

[Blank Page]

CGP

Key Stage Two

English

SATS Practice Papers Instructions & Answer Book

Contents

Exam Set EHPP24

Practice is the best way to prepare for the KS2 English SATs...

...and this brilliant pack of CGP Practice Papers has been fine-tuned to be a perfect match for the SATs in 2017 and beyond!

It contains two full sets of tests, each including a reading paper and two grammar, punctuation and spelling papers — just like the real test pupils will take in Year 6.

We've also included answers and mark schemes in this booklet. That means it's easy to find out which areas are their strongest, and where they need to concentrate their revision ahead of the SATs.

Test Contents

There are **two sets** of practice papers in this pack.
Each set has:

Reading Test   50 marks
1 hour
(reading booklet, and question and answer booklet)

Grammar, Punctuation and Spelling Paper 1 — Questions   50 marks
45 minutes
(question and answer booklet)

Grammar, Punctuation and Spelling Paper 2 — Spelling Task   20 marks
About 15 minutes
(pull-out question and answer booklet found in the middle of Grammar, Punctuation and Spelling Paper 1)

The Spelling Task needs to be read out to the child sitting the test.
The Spelling Task Scripts can be found on pages 15 and 16 of this booklet.

Published by CGP

Editors: Izzy Bowen, Emma Cleasby, Heather Gregson, Holly Poynton, Frances Rooney, Rebecca Tate, Matt Topping.

Contributor: Paul Warnes

With thanks to Emma Bonney and Rebecca Tate for the proofreading.
Also thanks to Ana Pungartnik for the copyright research.

Acknowledgements for Answer Booklet
National Curriculum references on page 4 reproduced under the terms of the Open Government Licence v3.0. http://www.nationalarchives.gov.uk/doc/open-government-licence/version/3/

Acknowledgements for Reading Set A:
With thanks to iStock.com for permission to use the images on pages 1, 2, 3, 4, 5, 6, 7, 8, 10, 11 and 12.

Acknowledgements for Reading Set B:
With thanks to iStock.com for permission to use the images on pages 1, 2, 3, 4, 7, 8, 9, 10, 11 and 12.

Clipart from Corel®
Printed by Elanders Ltd, Newcastle upon Tyne.

Text, design, layout and original illustrations
© Coordination Group Publications Ltd. (CGP) 2016
All rights reserved.

What the Questions Test

There are 8 different elements which can be assessed in the reading paper. Together they form the content domain for the reading test. They are linked to the national curriculum programme of study for Key Stage 2.

For every answer, we've included the element that is being tested.

They are:

2a: Give / explain the meaning of words in context.

2b: Retrieve and record information / identify key details from fiction and non-fiction.

2c: Summarise main ideas from more than one paragraph.

2d: Make inferences from the text / explain and justify inferences with evidence from the text.

2e: Predict what might happen from details stated and implied.

2f: Identify / explain how information / narrative content is related and contributes to meaning as a whole.

2g: Identify / explain how meaning is enhanced through choice of words and phrases.

2h: Make comparisons within the text.

Marking the Tests

The scores for these practice papers will give you a pretty good idea of whether a pupil is on track to achieve the **expected standard** in **Reading** and in **Grammar, Punctuation and Spelling**.

Reading

There's a total of **50** marks available.

The mark needed to achieve the **expected standard** varies from year to year, but if they get a total of **21** or more then they should be on track.

Grammar, Punctuation and Spelling

	Marks available
Paper 1: Short Answer Questions	50
Paper 2: Spelling Task	20
Total:	**70**

Add up the marks in the two papers to give a score out of **70**. Again, the mark needed to achieve the **expected standard** varies from year to year, but if they get a total of **44** or more then they should be on track. (The writing element of the national curriculum is assessed by the class teacher.)

<u>*Reading Set A — Answers*</u>

<u>Section 1 — Deserts</u>	
1 a) 250 mm. *(2b)*	**1 mark**
b) vast and sandy. *(2d)*	**1 mark**
c) –89°C *(2b)*	**1 mark**
d) seal. *(2b)*	**1 mark**
2 *1 mark for a suitable definition, e.g. "difficult to live in". (2a)*	**1 mark**
3 Fog from the Pacific Ocean brings moisture, which is 'life-saving'. *(2b)*	**1 mark**
4 *1 mark for a sensible answer, e.g. "Lots of people know what a rabbit looks like, so it helps them imagine what a viscacha looks like." (2d)*	**1 mark**
5 *1 mark for a suitable answer, e.g. "The sand dunes are very interesting." (2a)*	**1 mark**
6 Antarctica is full of snow, while the Arabian Desert is full of sand. Antarctica is very cold, while the Arabian Desert can get very hot. Ice crystals fall in Antarctica instead of water drops like in the Arabian Desert. *(1 mark for any correct difference) (2h)*	**1 mark**
7 The Atacama Desert borders the Atlantic Ocean. — False Cactuses are the only plants that can survive in the Atacama Desert. — False Sand dunes are formed by the wind. — True The biggest area of sand in the world is the Atacama Desert. — False *(1 mark for all 4 correct) (2b)*	**1 mark**
8 Penguins have oily feathers to repel water. Seals have blubber or fat to keep them warm. Small mammals have large ears to hear predators and keep cool. Some lizards have long toes to stop them sinking into sand. Some lizards have fat tails to store energy in. Arabian Oryx are small so can shelter under small trees. Arabian Oryx can walk long distances to find food and water. *(2 marks for any 2 correct adaptations) (2b)*	**2 marks**
9 a) *1 mark for a suitable theme, e.g. "Deserts are difficult to survive in" or "Deserts suffer extreme temperatures." (2c)*	**1 mark**
b) *1 mark for an appropriate supporting phrase, e.g. "harsh climate". (2b)*	**1 mark**

<u>Section 2 — Dishes Around the World</u>	
10 its crops *and* its spices *(1 mark for both correct) (2b)*	**1 mark**
11 *1 mark for a sensible answer, e.g. "It makes you feel excited because the word 'let's' makes you feel included." (2d)*	**1 mark**
12 Italy: wheat, maize, rice, olives, lemons India: wheat, rice, millet *(1 mark for two or three <u>different</u> crops, 2 marks for four <u>different</u> crops) (2b)*	**2 marks**
13 Italy *or* India *(2b)*	**1 mark**
14 closeness *(2a)*	**1 mark**
15 sushi *(2b)*	**1 mark**
16 *1 mark for a sensible answer, e.g. "Italians might not make pizza." (2d)*	**1 mark**
17 Cuisine can be influenced by other countries. *(2c)*	**1 mark**
18 *1 mark for making a simple comparison, e.g. "Both cuisines have lots of rice dishes." 2 marks for a more developed answer, e.g. "Japanese cuisine has a lot of seafood dishes, but many Indians are vegetarians so many of their dishes don't contain meat. Both countries grow rice, so it is used a lot in both Indian and Japanese dishes." (2h)*	**2 marks**
19 Lemons are grown in southern Italy. — Fact Japan is made up of thousands of islands. — Fact The tomato is the most important ingredient in Italian cuisine. — Opinion The spices added to Indian dishes make them delicious. — Opinion *(1 mark for all 4 correct) (2d)*	**1 mark**

20	Fish and chips Chicken tikka masala _(2b)_	**1 mark**
21	A lot of _or_ many. Money. _(1 mark for each correct definition) (2a)_	**2 marks**
22	_1 mark for a simple answer based on the text, e.g._ "The reader feels excited because there are lots of different dishes to try." _2 marks for a more detailed answer, e.g._ "The text makes the reader interested to try different dishes, since it says that there are lots of tempting dishes to try. The wide range of spices that are on offer in countries like India is also exciting." _3 marks for a more developed answer which refers in detail to the text, e.g._ "The text makes the reader feel excited about the dishes that are on offer in different countries and their different regions, because it talks about the tempting range of dishes in Italy and the exciting seafood that's on offer in Japan. The text also says that these dishes are good value, which makes the reader feel that this is something most people can experience. The end of the text includes the phrase 'test your taste buds', which encourages the reader and makes them feel determined to try food from around the world." _(2d)_	**3 marks**

Section 3 — Kidnapped

23	_1 mark for a sensible answer, e.g._ "To summarise the story so far and show where the extract fits into the story as a whole". _(2f)_	**1 mark**
24	David _(2d)_	**1 mark**
25	deafening roaring thrashing thundering cries _(1 mark for any 3 words) (2g)_	**1 mark**
26	_1 mark for a suitable answer, e.g._ "That he has been kidnapped and is trapped on the ship." _(2b)_	**1 mark**
27	_1 mark for a sensible answer, e.g._ "Worried about what will happen to David". _(2d)_	**1 mark**
28	_1 mark for a suitable answer, e.g._ "The text says he was 'bereft' of his senses" _or_ "He 'returned again to life', which means that he woke up after fainting." _(2d)_	**1 mark**
29	(many) hardships _(2a)_	**1 mark**
30	release _(2a)_	**1 mark**
31	_1 mark for a simple answer, e.g._ "The captain fired the guns because the ship was going past the place where it was built." _or_ "The captain fired the guns to mark the fact that they were passing the place where his mother lived." _(2d)_	**1 mark**
32	a) He tries to see the best in people. _(2c)_ b) _1 mark for a sensible phrase, e.g._ "to show that even the worst man may have his kindlier side". _(2d)_	**1 mark** **1 mark**
33	It suggests that this part of the ship is dark _or_ It suggests that there is no sunlight. _(2d)_	**1 mark**
34	_1 mark for a suitable answer, e.g._ "He thinks the ship will sink." _(2d)_	**1 mark**
35	_1 mark for a simple answer, e.g._ "At the end of the extract, David is being looked after by someone." _2 marks for a more developed answer, e.g._ "At the end of the extract, David has come to his senses and someone else on the ship is helping him by seeing to his wounds." _(2c)_	**2 marks**
36	_1 mark for a basic prediction, e.g._ "He will not speak to the man and will be left in the cabin." _2 marks for a more developed answer with a full explanation, e.g._ "The ship will sink because of the storm and David will be shipwrecked on an island." _3 marks for a more detailed prediction which is fully supported with details from the text, e.g._ "David will stop crying and talk to the man because he seems friendly and has tried to talk to David. The extract says 'as I was afterwards told' which suggests that David will meet the captain and his crew and talk to them." _(2e)_	**3 marks**

<u>Reading Set B — Answers</u>

<u>Section 1 — All About Mice</u>

1	Mice tend to live for between 1.5 and 3 years. — Fact It is great to have a mouse for a pet. — Opinion Before getting a mouse, you should learn the facts. — Opinion Mice eat both plants and animals. — Fact *(1 mark for all answers correct)* *(2d)*	**1 mark**
2	They are easily frightened by noise. *(2b)*	**1 mark**
3	The dust can hurt the mouse's lungs. *(2b)*	**1 mark**
4	"fresh drinking water should be constantly available" *(2d)*	**1 mark**
5	*1 mark for a suitable answer, e.g.* "goodness" *or* "nutrients" *(2a)*	**1 mark**
6	*1 mark for a sensible answer, e.g.* "They might only eat their favourite parts of the food, so may not get enough nourishment." *(2d)*	**1 mark**
7	crisps *and* grapes *(1 mark for both correct answers)* *(2b)*	**1 mark**
8	The mouse might be allergic to the food. *(2b)*	**1 mark**
9	crucial *(2a)*	**1 mark**
10	*1 mark for a sensible answer, e.g.* "It suggests that they care about their mice as they want them to be able to run in a more natural way." *(2d)*	**1 mark**
11	*1 mark for any sensible item with an explanation or two items with no explanation, e.g.* "Loose material so they can burrow". *2 marks for a more detailed answer with two items, both with an explanation, e.g.* "Chew toys to keep their teeth short and a wheel so they can exercise and keep healthy". *(2b)*	**2 marks**
12	*1 mark for a simple answer giving one difference, e.g.* "An ill mouse might weigh less than a healthy mouse." *2 marks for a more developed answer giving two separate differences, e.g.* "An ill mouse might be less active than a healthy mouse. An ill mouse might also have fur that is rough or spiky, whilst a healthy mouse will have smooth fur." *(2d)*	**2 marks**
13	*1 mark for a suitable answer, e.g.* "It refers to choosing the correct pet, which is mentioned in the introduction." *(2f)*	**1 mark**
14	*1 mark for a sensible answer, e.g.* "It suggests that looking after a mouse is hard work." *(2g)*	**1 mark**
15	That people should be well informed before buying a mouse *(2c)*	**1 mark**

<u>Section 2 — An Amsterdam Adventure</u>

16	*1 mark for a sensible reason, e.g.* "The ferry journey had made her feel sick." *(2d)*	**1 mark**
17	*1 mark for a sensible answer, e.g.* "They got stuck in traffic." *(2b)*	**1 mark**
18	*1 mark for a sensible answer, e.g.* "They are really tall." *(2g)*	**1 mark**
19	brightly coloured *(2a)*	**1 mark**
20	*1 mark for a sensible answer, e.g.* "That the park is very large and covers lots of ground." *(2g)*	**1 mark**
21	You get there via a side street. It's noisy. It's near a canal. It's wide. You can smell food cooking. It's busy / full of people There are lots of stalls. It's cobbled. *(1 mark for 3 correct answers)* *(2b)*	**1 mark**
22	focused *(2a)*	**1 mark**
23	bitternballen *(2b)*	**1 mark**

Reading Set B — Answers

24	*1 mark for a simple answer, e.g.* "She really liked the market." *2 marks for a more developed answer which refers directly to the text, e.g.* "Sophie really liked the market as she was 'taken aback' at the sight of it and tried 'delicious' food from the stalls." *3 marks for a more detailed response which makes three separate points, e.g.* "Sophie was excited even before she reached the market as she and her mum could hear it before they could see it. When she saw the market she was 'taken aback' by the sight of it, which shows that she thought it was impressive. She described the market as 'alive' and used positive words to describe the things on sale like 'delicate' and 'delicious'. This shows that she enjoyed spending time at the market." *(2d)*	**3 marks**
25	A popular tourist destination *(2d)*	**1 mark**
26	*1 mark for a sensible definition, e.g.* "useless" *or* "pointless" *(2a)*	**1 mark**
27	*1 mark for a suitable comparison, e.g.* "The canal tour was much more relaxing than the ferry" *or* "The canal ride was much smoother and didn't make Sophie feel sick." *(2h)*	**1 mark**
28	*1 mark for a simple answer, e.g.* "They wouldn't visit the Van Gogh museum because it was so busy." *2 marks for a more developed answer which makes two predictions with reasons, e.g.* "They would travel to Amsterdam in a different way because the ferry made Sophie feel sick and the coach took a long time. They also wouldn't go to the Van Gogh museum because it was so busy that they couldn't see the art." *(2e)*	**2 marks**
29	Sophie tries local food. — 4 Sophie receives a gift. — 3 Sophie admires stained glass windows. — 1 Sophie goes to a lake. — 2 Sophie visits a museum. — 5 *(1 mark for all 4 correct) (2f)*	**1 mark**

Section 3 — Tales From Outer Space

30	videophone *(2b)*	**1 mark**
31	man-made *(2a)*	**1 mark**
32	Astronomer *(2b)*	**1 mark**
33	5 years *(2b)*	**1 mark**
34	*1 mark for a suitable answer, e.g.* "She is an expert on Mars." *(2d)*	**1 mark**
35	*1 mark for a sensible answer, e.g.* "The results aren't affected by the gases in the Earth's atmosphere." *(2d)*	**1 mark**
36	An astronaut is trained mostly in space. — False The WSS is going to land on Mars next year. — False You can see the Earth from the WSS. — True Astronauts choose their own food. — False *(1 mark for 4 correct answers) (2c)*	**1 mark**
37	*1 mark for a suitable definition in this context, e.g.* "organised" *or* "strictly controlled". *(2a)*	**1 mark**
38	*1 mark for a suitable answer, e.g.* "Her grandfather bought her a telescope." *(2d)*	**1 mark**
39	Florida *(2b)*	**1 mark**
40	*1 mark for a sensible answer, e.g.* "It makes the reader feel excited and slightly nervous" *or* "It makes the reader feel scared because the rockets are so loud". *(2d)*	**1 mark**
41	Madeleine has spent two months on the WSS. — Fact Robots have been sent to Mars. — Fact Daydreaming won't make you successful. — Opinion Being an astronaut is worth the intense training. — Opinion *(1 mark for all 4 correct) (2d)*	**1 mark**
42	a) Becoming an astronaut is hard work. *(2c)*	**1 mark**
	b) *1 mark for a sensible explanation, e.g.* "There are many references to hard work in the text, like 'intense training' and 'extensive knowledge'. The conclusion links back to this idea, talking about the 'painstaking' effort needed to become an astronaut." *(2b)*	**1 mark**
43	*1 mark for choosing an answer and supporting the choice with a simple statement, e.g.* "It makes you feel like being an astronaut would be really exciting." *2 marks for making 2 points to support the choice, e.g.* "It makes you feel that the life of an astronaut is hard work, because you need to be physically fit. It also seems exciting because you can go to space and see amazing things like the oceans on Earth." *(2d)*	**2 marks**

Grammar, Punctuation and Spelling Set A Paper 1 — Answers

1	All of the pupils like English, and most of them also enjoy maths, art, science and sport. (*1 mark for both correct*)	**1 mark**
2		

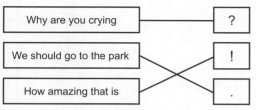

	(*1 mark for all 3 correct*)	**1 mark**
3	*Panting and out of breath, Phil crossed the finish line.*	**1 mark**
4	*We were talking about going to Majorca on holiday.*	**1 mark**
5	• boiling water • a splash of milk • two sugar cubes (*1 mark for all 3 correct — if the answer uses capitalisation, it should do so at the start of each point. If the answer uses punctuation, it should use either commas or semi-colons after the first two points and a full stop after the third.*)	**1 mark**
6	*are they*	**1 mark**
7	*do, trevor, i'm* (*1 mark for all 3 correct*)	**1 mark**
8	*is was*	**1 mark**
9	You should have circled *My sister*. You should have underlined *a heavy parcel*.	**1 mark**
10	Answers may vary; accept any suitable questions, e.g.	

Question	Answer
What do you like to eat at the cinema?	Popcorn.
How many chairs are there at the table?	There are twelve.
What does Martha do after school?	She sings.

	(*1 mark for both correct*)	**1 mark**
11	*hasn't, it's, we'll* (*1 mark for all 3 correct*)	**1 mark**
12	*or* and *but* (*1 mark for both correct*)	**1 mark**
13	Answers may vary; accept any suitable antonyms, e.g. *cowardly* and *lazy* (*1 mark for both correct*)	**1 mark**
14	*Cut up the vegetables into chunks.* *Serve with some soy sauce.* (*1 mark for both correct*)	**1 mark**
15	*mine, yours, hers* (*1 mark for all 3 correct*)	**1 mark**
16	*She* and *It* (*1 mark for both correct*)	**1 mark**
17		

Sentence	Modal verb shows **possibility**	Modal verb shows **certainty**
Mairi might come and visit in a few weeks.	✓	
Josh will play better than that.		✓
Helen and Keith may be coming for dinner.	✓	
I shall arrive at seven o'clock in the morning.		✓

	(*1 mark for all 4 correct*)	**1 mark**

18	Louise liked reading books, so she often went to the library in town. ↑ ✓	
		1 mark
19	sings ⟶ **sang** beg ⟶ **begged** says ⟶ **said** *(1 mark for all 3 correct)*	
		1 mark
20	We got there just in time the show was about to begin. ↑ ✓	
		1 mark
21	Answers may vary; accept any two suitable explanations, e.g. The votes were <u>miscounted</u>. This means that the votes *were counted incorrectly.* The votes were <u>recounted</u>. This means that the votes *were counted again.* *(1 mark for both correct)*	
		1 mark
22	*had*	1 mark
23	*an exclamation*	1 mark
24	*After*	1 mark
25	*much* and *the* *(1 mark for both correct)*	1 mark
26	Anthony said, "The new museum is full of interesting exhibits."	1 mark
27	a) Answers may vary; accept any suitable explanation, e.g. *A word that means the same or nearly the same as another word.*	1 mark
	b) Answers may vary, e.g. *cross* or *furious*	1 mark
28	<u>Although I like cars</u>, I didn't enjoy visiting the transport museum. <u>Despite being tired</u>, Sonia tried her best in the running race. Callie watched television <u>while Allan did his homework</u>. *(1 mark for all 3 correct)*	
		1 mark
29		

Sentence	Adjective	Adverb
He walked down the **narrow** street.	✓	
Make sure you stay **close**.		✓
Andrew hit the ball **hard**.		✓
I gave her a **challenging** task.	✓	

	(1 mark for all 4 correct)	1 mark
30	The hare chased Harry — my best friend — across the park.	1 mark
31	-al and -ian *(1 mark for both correct)*	1 mark
32	The car was repaired by Vicky.	1 mark
33	which are in the tin	1 mark
34	Ian and Leah were dancing together.	1 mark
35	Saeed has every sticker in the album, but soon we will have them all too. ↑C ↑B ↑D ↑A	
	(1 mark for all 4 correct)	1 mark

36	*who*	**1 mark**

37 Answers may vary; accept any suitable noun phrases, e.g.

Noun	Noun Phrase
the cushion	the fluffy cushion on my bed
the house	<u>the bright orange house behind the school</u>

1 mark

38 *The first sentence suggests Urvi collects two things: jam and mice made from chocolate.*
The second sentence suggests Urvi collects three things: jam, mice and chocolate. **1 mark**

39 *Ben wanted to drive — he knew the route.* **1 mark**

40 *Before lunch, we said goodbye to Gran.* **1 mark**

41 *Once we'd found the missing piece, <u>we finally finished the jigsaw</u>.*
<u>*Toby went home*</u> *after we'd eaten our picnic.*
Before you go swimming, <u>don't forget to feed the rabbits</u>.
<u>*He tried to fix the tyre*</u> *that the dog had bitten.*
(1 mark for all 4 correct) **1 mark**

42 *The doctor saw forty nine-year-olds in one day.* **1 mark**

43 *although* **1 mark**

44 *noun* **1 mark**

45 *carry* **1 mark**

46 *were* **1 mark**

47 *Christina packed a tube of suncream; a large, frilly hat; and a pair of sunglasses.* **1 mark**

48

Sentence	Co-ordinating conjunction	Subordinating conjunction
Moeen goes swimming **and** diving.	✓	
I will only go **if** the weather is nice.		✓
You can call me tonight, **or** you can call me tomorrow night.	✓	

(1 mark for all 3 correct) **1 mark**

49

Sentence	Noun phrase	Subordinate clause
My dog is good at chasing rabbits **because she's so quick**.		✓
The grumpy woman plodded along the street.	✓	
Everyone was jealous of **Claire's new running shoes**.	✓	
Eugene listened to the radio **while his wife had a nap.**		✓

(1 mark for all 4 correct) **1 mark**

1

Word	Verb	Adjective
fast		✓
attend	✓	
cycle	✓	
shiny		✓

(1 mark for all 4 correct) **1 mark**

2 Running is a great sport Ian often goes running in York with his sister.

✓ **1 mark**

3 "Come back here" shouted Tom as Zak marched away from him.

✓ **1 mark**

4 *last, harriet, the* and *august* *(1 mark for all 4 correct)* **1 mark**

5

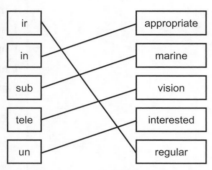

(1 mark for all 5 correct) **1 mark**

6 *You haven't seen it already, have you* **1 mark**

7 *youngest* and *rusty* *(1 mark for both correct)* **1 mark**

8 *"Put your pencils away," said the teacher.* **1 mark**

9 Answers may vary, for example: *What <u>time is it?</u>*
(1 mark for a grammatically correct question ending with a question mark.) **1 mark**

10 *worked* and *was* *(1 mark for both correct)* **1 mark**

11 *cakes* **1 mark**

12 *and, but, before, so* and *once* *(1 mark for all 5 correct)* **1 mark**

13 *on* **1 mark**

14 he is ──→ **he's**
could not ──→ **couldn't**
I am ──→ **I'm**
will not ──→ **won't**
(1 mark for all 4 correct) **1 mark**

15 *we, us* and *them* *(1 mark for all 3 correct)* **1 mark**

16 When I was six years old, we made a non stop journey to Tokyo.

✓ **1 mark**

17 *broken* and *enjoyable* *(1 mark for both correct)* **1 mark**

Grammar, Punctuation and Spelling Set B Paper 1 — Answers

18	*grand*	**1 mark**
19	*mine*	**1 mark**
20	Answers may vary; accept any suitable formal synonym, e.g. *delighted*.	**1 mark**
21	*The thief, who was very crafty, stole money, rings and a painting.*	**1 mark**
22	Answers may vary; accept any suitable antonyms, e.g. *strong* and *stressful* *(1 mark for both correct)*	**1 mark**
23	a) *dashes*	**1 mark**
	b) *brackets* or *commas*	**1 mark**

24

Sentence	Main clause	Subordinate clause
There was a rainbow **even though it wasn't raining**.		✓
Since there was nothing to do, the boys were very bored.		✓
Before the tide came in, **we packed the picnic away**.	✓	

(1 mark for all 3 correct)   **1 mark**

25   *Ashleigh caught a fish.*

S   V   O

(1 mark for all 3 correct)   **1 mark**

26	*that*	**1 mark**
27	*Before the performance, Sam was content and relaxed.*	**1 mark**
28	*While they helped, Sarah, Thomas and Joe Smith chatted about their holiday.*	**1 mark**
29	*The weather was bad — awful actually — so I stayed indoors.*	**1 mark**

30   to play ⟶ **am playing**
to win ⟶ **is winning**
(1 mark for both correct)   **1 mark**

31   <u>Before we could park</u>, we drove around for twenty minutes.
I don't like car racing <u>because the cars are too loud</u>.
Nilam went skating <u>after she took the dog for a walk</u>.
<u>When I grow up</u>, I want to be a vet.
(1 mark for all 4 correct)   **1 mark**

32   *a, every, My* and *the*
(1 mark for all 4 correct)   **1 mark**

| 33 | *very* | **1 mark** |

34   *That castle which was built by the Normans is still standing today.*

✓

1 mark

35

Sentence	Statement	Command
You can use the hose to wash the car.	✓	
When you have finished, tidy away the hose and sponges.		✓
If the car is really clean, Dad will give you extra pocket money.	✓	

(1 mark for all 3 correct)   **1 mark**

36	*a noun phrase*	1 mark
37	Answers may vary; accept any suitable sentence that is correctly punctuated, e.g. *You should show Peter your photo album.* (1 mark for a suitable sentence)	1 mark
	Answers may vary; accept any suitable sentence that is correctly punctuated, e.g. *Mandy took Neil to see a show at the theatre.* (1 mark for a suitable sentence)	1 mark
38	*colon* or *ellipsis (...)* or *dash*	1 mark

39

Sentence	Subject	Object
I love **you**.		✓
The new computer is great.	✓	
His favourite sport is **tennis**.		✓
My grandmother welcomed the guests.	✓	

(1 mark for all 4 correct) — **1 mark**

40 a) *Its, Andrews*

b) Possible answers: *Its — It is a contraction of 'it is'. The apostrophe shows omission.*
Andrews — The shoe size belongs to Andrew. The apostrophe shows possession.
(1 mark for correct words and a correct explanation) — **1 mark**

41 <u>The oak tree at the bottom of the garden</u> *has been there for two hundred years.* — **1 mark**

42

Sentence	Preposition	Subordinating conjunction
Count sheep **until** you fall asleep.		✓
Until he apologises, I'm not talking to him.		✓
The shop is closed **until** 8 am.	✓	

(1 mark for all 3 correct) — **1 mark**

43	*I will bake some biscuits.*	1 mark
44	Answers may vary; accept any suitable word that begins with the prefix 'tri-', e.g. *triangle, tricycle.*	1 mark
45	*Jamal had sent his friend a letter, but he did not expect a reply.*	1 mark
46	*The big hamburger was eaten by Julian.*	1 mark
47	Answers may vary; accept any suitable sentence that lists all the information given and is punctuated correctly, e.g. *The shopping list consists of washing-up liquid, sponges, a present (for Michael) and potatoes.*	1 mark
48	*were*	1 mark

Instructions for the Spelling Task

Each test should take about 15 minutes to do, but you can give the children as much time as they need. Read out the following instructions, and then answer any questions the children may have.

- *Listen to the instructions I'm about to give you.*
- *I'm going to read out twenty sentences. These sentences are printed in your answer booklet, but each one has a word missing. Listen to the missing word and write it in. Make sure you spell it correctly.*
- *I will read the word, then read the word within a sentence, then I'll say the word a third time.*
- *Have you got any questions?*

Now read the spellings to the children:

- Say the spelling number
- Say *"The word is..."*
- Read out the word in its sentence.
- Say *"The word is..."*
- Pause for at least 12 seconds between each of the spellings.

At the end of the test, read out all 20 sentences again, and give the children time to change their answers if they want to.

When the test is over, say "This is the end of the test."

Spelling Task Set A — script/answers

Spelling one — the word is **shrink**. *I am worried that my jeans will **shrink**.* The word is **shrink**.

Spelling two — the word is **batteries**. *The spare **batteries** are in that drawer.* The word is **batteries**.

Spelling three — the word is **touch**. *If I stretch my arms, I can **touch** the ceiling.* The word is **touch**.

Spelling four — the word is **forty**. *The bus is **forty** minutes late.* The word is **forty**.

Spelling five — the word is **possibly**. *He was **possibly** the best basketball player in the school.* The word is **possibly**.

Spelling six — the word is **adorable**. *Olivia's new rabbit is **adorable**.* The word is **adorable**.

Spelling seven — the word is **bought**. *Kevin **bought** some oranges at the market.* The word is **bought**.

Spelling eight — the word is **familiar**. *She thought the man looked **familiar**.* The word is **familiar**.

Spelling nine — the word is **persuade**. *I tried to **persuade** them to come swimming.* The word is **persuade**.

Spelling ten — the word is **equipment**. *The girls packed the **equipment** ready for the field trip.* The word is **equipment**.

Spelling eleven — the word is **evidence**. *There was **evidence** that the man was guilty.* The word is **evidence**.

Spelling twelve — the word is **preferred**. *I **preferred** learning German to French.* The word is **preferred**.

Spelling thirteen — the word is **reign**. *At the start of her **reign**, the Queen threw a big party.* The word is **reign**.

0815 - 13606

Grammar, Punctuation and Spelling Paper 2 — Scripts/Answers

Spelling fourteen — the word is **co-owner**. *She is a co-owner of the company.* The word is **co-owner**.

Spelling fifteen — the word is **controversy**. *Raj's new, orange door caused much controversy.* The word is **controversy**.

Spelling sixteen — the word is **essential**. *A warm coat is essential in this terrible weather.* The word is **essential**.

Spelling seventeen — the word is **island**. *Jamie lives on a tropical island.* The word is **island**.

Spelling eighteen — the word is **accept**. *I will accept the award on Tuesday.* The word is **accept**.

Spelling nineteen — the word is **weary**. *By the evening, everyone was tired and weary.* The word is **weary**.

Spelling twenty — the word is **amateur**. *My friend is an amateur footballer.* The word is **amateur**.

Spelling Task Set B — script/answers

Spelling one — the word is **tasted**. *I tasted seaweed for the first time today.* The word is **tasted**.

Spelling two — the word is **describe**. *My teacher asked me to describe my pets.* The word is **describe**.

Spelling three — the word is **unclear**. *My writing is always unclear when I rush.* The word is **unclear**.

Spelling four — the word is **happily**. *He walked happily along the beach.* The word is **happily**.

Spelling five — the word is **calendar**. *Eric wrote the date of the party on his calendar.* The word is **calendar**.

Spelling six — the word is **business**. *One day, Jemma will own her own business.* The word is **business**.

Spelling seven — the word is **accompany**. *Sandy will accompany Eddie to the wedding.* The word is **accompany**.

Spelling eight — the word is **chef**. *My mum is the chef at this restaurant.* The word is **chef**.

Spelling nine — the word is **completely**. *Sanjay completely forgot to send the letter.* The word is **completely**.

Spelling ten — the word is **suggest**. *I suggest that you go to the zoo during the holidays.* The word is **suggest**.

Spelling eleven — the word is **crucial**. *Stan is a crucial member of the rowing team.* The word is **crucial**.

Spelling twelve — the word is **substance**. *The sweets are filled with a sugary substance.* The word is **substance**.

Spelling thirteen — the word is **version**. *Which version of the game did you play?* The word is **version**.

Spelling fourteen — the word is **stomach**. *Sandra's stomach hurt after she drank lots of milk.* The word is **stomach**.

Spelling fifteen — the word is **achieve**. *It's amazing what you can achieve if you put your mind to it.* The word is **achieve**.

Spelling sixteen — the word is **league**. *Megan's football team is top of the league.* The word is **league**.

Spelling seventeen — the word is **collision**. *There was a collision between two rugby players.* The word is **collision**.

Spelling eighteen — the word is **partial**. *It is hard to see in this partial daylight.* The word is **partial**.

Spelling nineteen — the word is **conscious**. *Mark is conscious of the fact that time is running out.* The word is **conscious**.

Spelling twenty — the word is **yacht**. *She has learnt how to sail a yacht.* The word is **yacht**.

Mathematics
Key Stage 2

Set A
Practice Paper 1
Arithmetic

Calculator Not Allowed
30 minutes

First name	
Middle name	
Last name	
School	

Date of birth	Day		Month		Year	

CGP

1   489 × 1 =

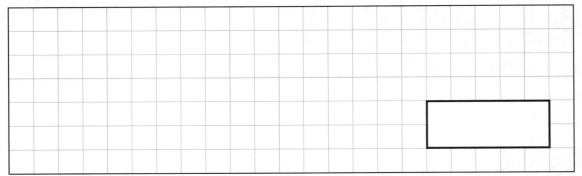

2   2253 + 1000 =

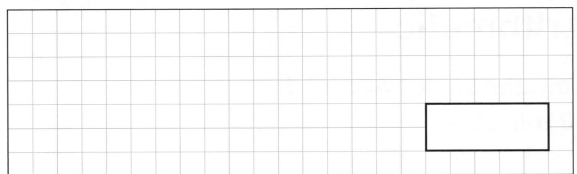

3   146 + 75 =

4   56 ÷ 8 =

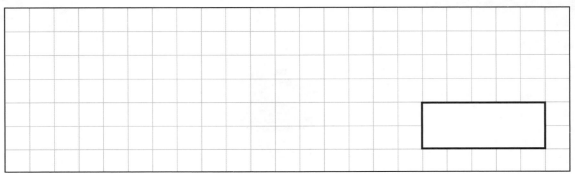

(5)  = 32 × 3

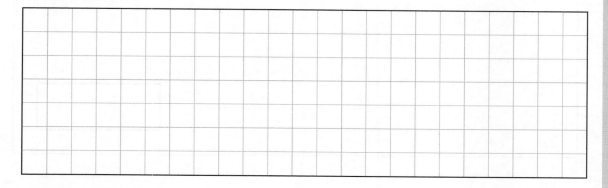

(6) 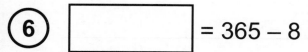 = 365 − 8

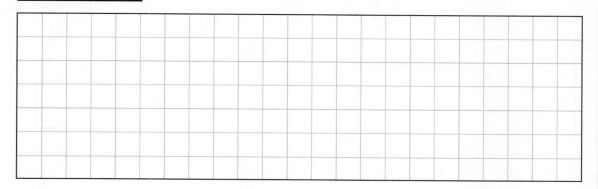

(7) 2 × 3 × 9 =

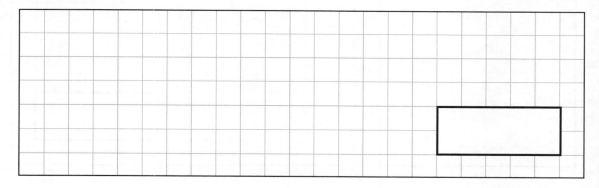

(8) -7 + 10 =

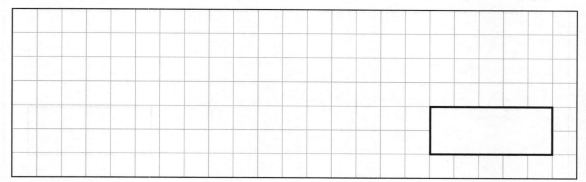

9 7.5 − 0.4 =

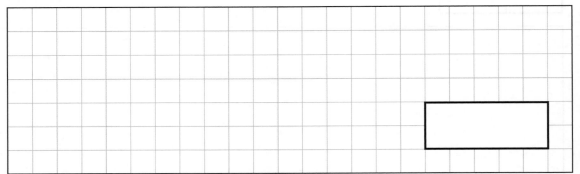

1 mark

10 49 992 + 6842 =

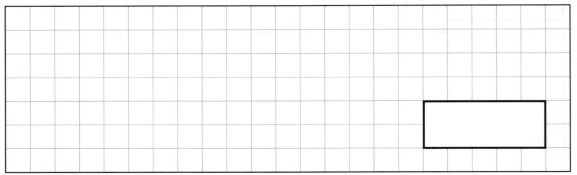

1 mark

11 3.2 + 0.03 =

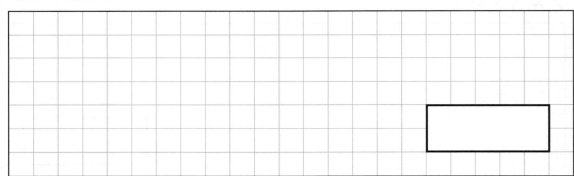

1 mark

12 1000 × 13 =

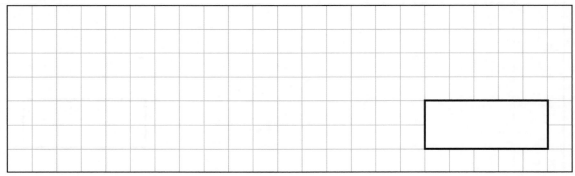

1 mark

13) 16 000 − 80 =

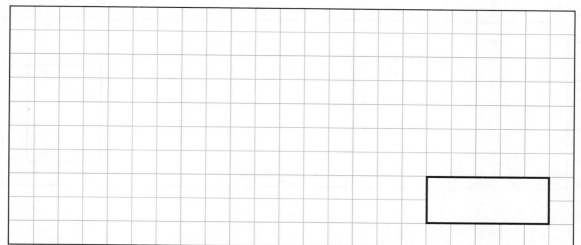

14) 17.26 × 10 =

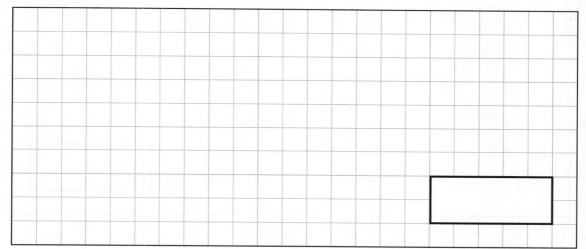

15) 917 × 6 =

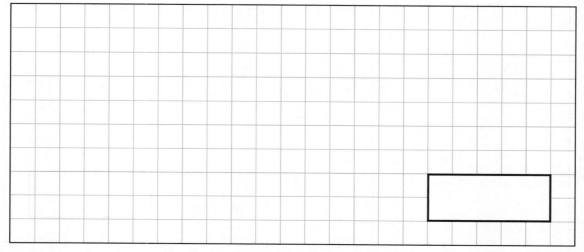

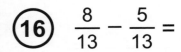

16 $\frac{8}{13} - \frac{5}{13} =$

1 mark

17 38 467 − 4623 =

1 mark

18 19.006 + 12.28 =

1 mark

19 9288 ÷ 9 =

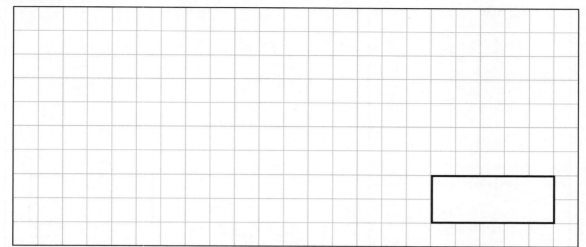

20 0.3 ÷ 10 =

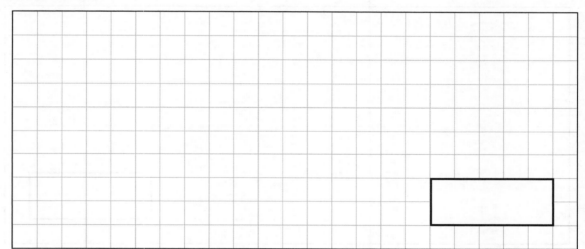

21 $5^2 - 3^2$ =

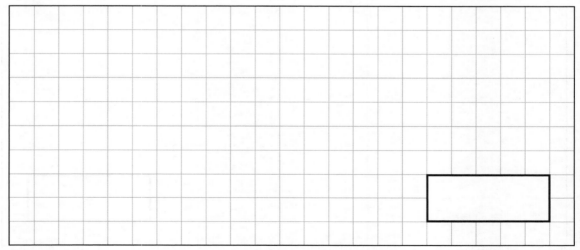

22 1080 ÷ 12 =

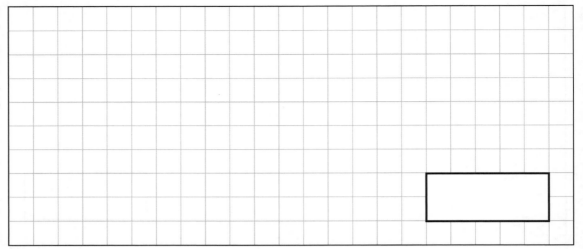

23 30% × 400 =

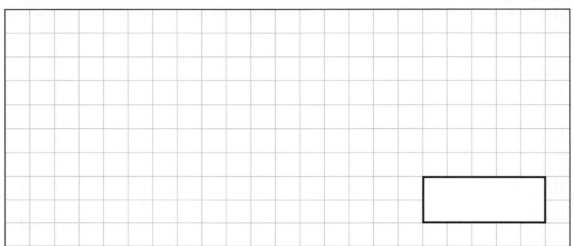

24 $\frac{4}{5}$ of 125 =

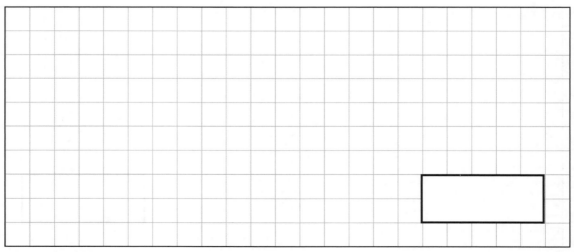

25

Show your working

$$\begin{array}{r} 8\ 5 \\ \times\ 2\ 8 \\ \hline \end{array}$$

2 marks

26 22.6 − 4.67 =

1 mark

27

Show your working

14) 4 8 0 2

2 marks

(28) 7 × (37 − 29) =

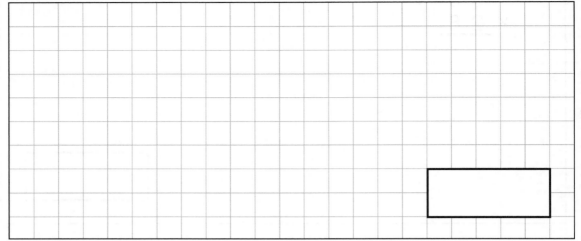

(29) 0.8 × 346 =

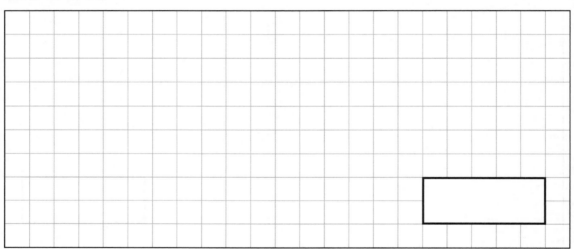

(30) 41% of 110 =

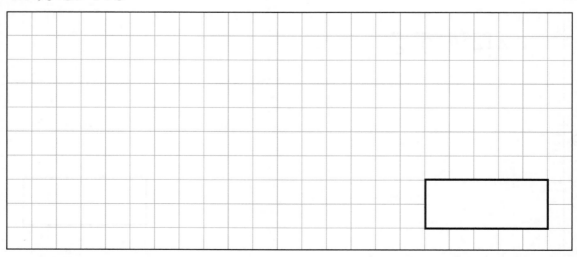

31 $\dfrac{3}{5} + \dfrac{7}{15} =$

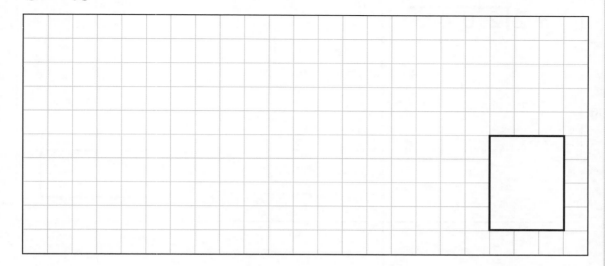

32

$$\begin{array}{r} 3\ 2\ 1\ 9 \\ \times\quad\ \ 5\ 3 \\ \hline \end{array}$$

Show your working

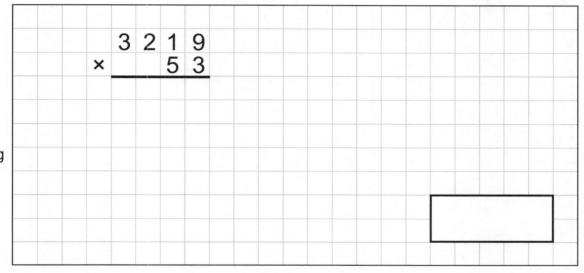

33 $\dfrac{6}{7} \div 3 =$

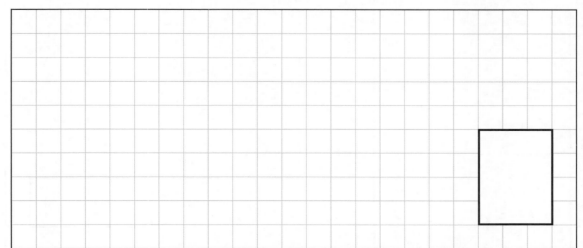

$$3\ 2\ \overline{|2\ 0\ 4\ 8}$$

Show your working

35 $1\frac{1}{4} + \frac{4}{5} =$

36 $1\frac{2}{7} \times 28 =$

2 mark

1 ma

1 ma

Mathematics
Key Stage 2

Total marks

Set A
Practice Paper 2
Reasoning

Calculator Not Allowed
40 minutes

First name	
Middle name	
Last name	
School	

Date of birth	Day		Month		Year	

CGP

1 Write these amounts of money in order starting with the **smallest**.

£0.72   27p   £2.70   £2.07   £2.77

smallest   largest

1 mark

2 Emily makes a pictogram to show the types of plant in her garden.

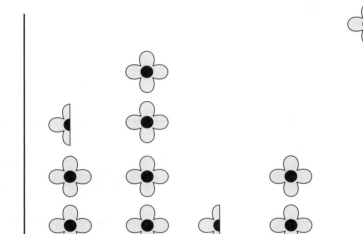 = 10 plants

Daffodils   Daisies   Roses   Petunias

How many **more** daisies than roses does Emily have?

1 mark

How many plants are there in Emily's garden in total?

1 mark

3 The shape below is made up of cubes. Each cube has a volume of 1 cm³.

What is the volume of the shape?

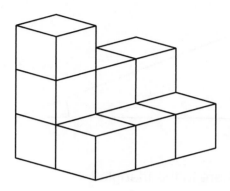

cm³

1 mark

 4 Hannah, Clare and James each buy a toy.

Hannah's toy costs **£1.25**.

Clare uses these coins to pay for her toy.

The **total** cost of the three toys is **£6**.

What is the cost of James's toy?

Show your working

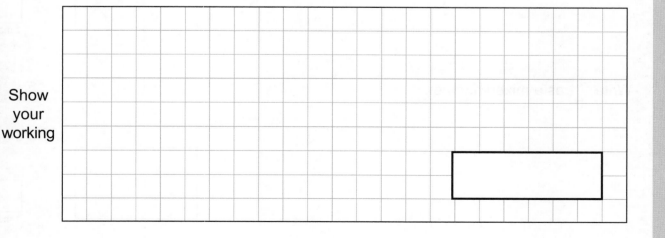

2 marks

5 Look at the triangle below.

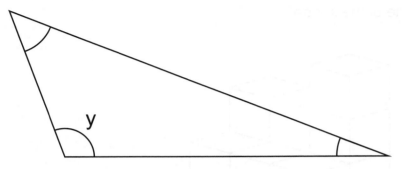

How many **acute** angles are there in the triangle?

1 mark

Use a protractor (angle measurer) to measure angle y.

°

1 mark

6 Write $4\frac{3}{7}$ as an improper fraction.

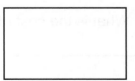

1 mark

Write $\frac{41}{6}$ as a mixed number.

1 mark

7 A group of friends do a maths quiz as quickly as possible.

This table shows the time it took each of them to finish the quiz.

Name	Olivia	Holly	Nikhil	Millie	Winston
Time (seconds)	120.5	137.2	122.0	135.6	120.8

Which pair of friends took a total of **258 seconds** to finish the quiz?

[ ] **and** [ ]

1 mark

How much longer did it take Holly to finish the quiz than Millie?

[ ] **seconds**

1 mark

What was Nikhil's time in minutes and seconds?

[ ] **minutes and** [ ] **seconds**

1 mark

8 Fill in the missing digits to make the calculation below correct.

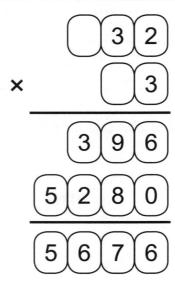

```
    ⬜ 3 2
  ×   ⬜ 3
  ─────────
    3 9 6
  5 2 8 0
  ─────────
  5 6 7 6
```

2 mark

 9 Write down an estimate that could be used to check the answer to the calculation below.

$$2.12 \times 58 = 122.96$$

⬜ × ⬜ = ⬜

1 mark

 10 Complete the following.

$$0.66 = \boxed{} \% = \dfrac{\boxed{}}{50}$$

2 marks

11 Grace and Habib go to a cafe for lunch.

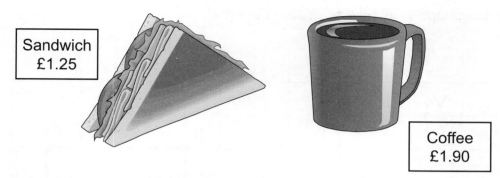

Sandwich £1.25

Coffee £1.90

They buy two coffees and some sandwiches.
The total bill is **£8.80**.

How many sandwiches do they buy?

Show your working

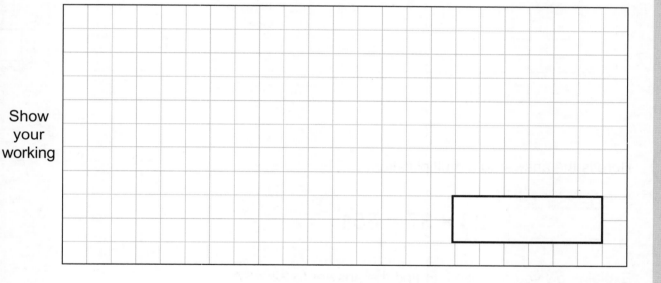

2 marks

12 The shape below is translated so that point X moves to point Y.

Redraw the shape in its new position on the grid.

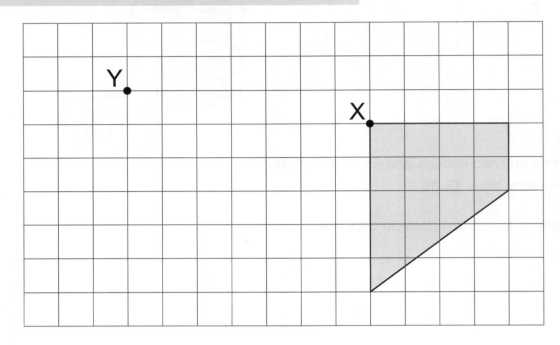

2 mark

13 Here is the answer to a multiplication.

$$23 × 37 = 851$$

Explain how you can use it to find the answer to **22 × 37**.

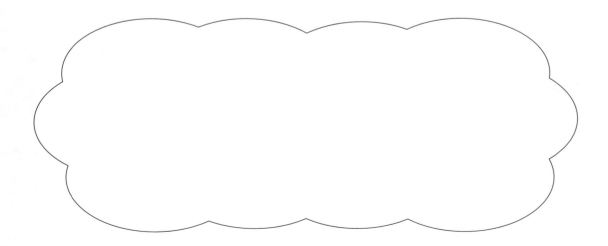

1 mar

Some parts of the rectangle below have been shaded grey.

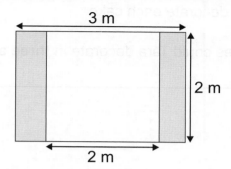

What is the **total** area of the **grey** parts of the rectangle?

Show your working

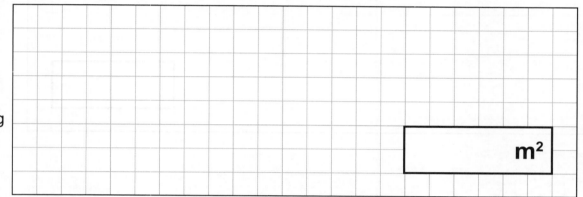

m^2

---

15 Circle a pair of numbers that are both factors of **24**, and which add together to give **another** factor of 24.

1   2   3   4   5   6   7   8   9

---

16 Tara is decorating cakes.
It takes her 16 minutes to decorate each cake.

How many **complete** cakes could Tara decorate in **three and a half hours**?

Show
your
working

2 marks

17 The symbols ▲, ● and ♥ below each stand for a different whole number.

$$▲ + ● × ♥ = 24$$

If ▲ = **6**, write down two different possible pairs of numbers for ● and ♥.

● =

♥ =

1 mark

● =

♥ =

1 mark

18 Circle the number that is the correct answer to the calculation.

20

| one million ÷ five hundred = |

200

2000

20 000

19 Patrick went cycling one weekend.
He cycled 12 fewer kilometres on Sunday than he cycled on Saturday.
He cycled **38 km** in total that weekend.

How many kilometres did he cycle on **Saturday**?

| | **km** |

Tom, Scott and Dawn sold cookies at the school fair.

Tom had **90** cookies and sold **60%** of them.

Scott had **150** cookies and sold $\frac{2}{3}$ of them.

Dawn sold **46** cookies.

What percentage of the **cookies sold** were sold by Dawn?

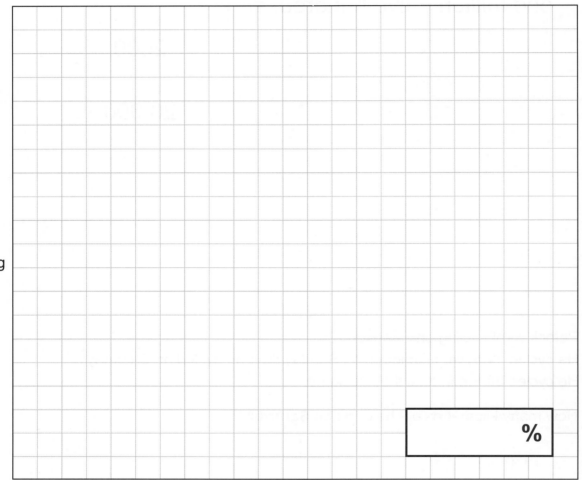

Show
your
working

%

3 marks

Mathematics
Key Stage 2

Set A
Practice Paper 3
Reasoning

Calculator Not Allowed
40 minutes

First name	
Middle name	
Last name	
School	

Date of birth	Day		Month		Year	

CGP

1 Write each of these as **numbers**.

Seventy-five thousand, two hundred and thirty-eight.

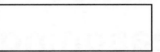

Four hundred and eighty-six thousand, two hundred and fourteen.

2 Part of a shape has been drawn below.

Complete the shape so that it is symmetrical about the mirror line.

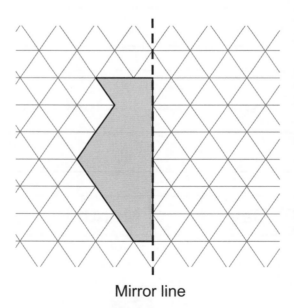

Mirror line

3 This table shows the temperature in different countries.

Country	Spain	Finland	Canada	France
Temperature	14°C	-8°C	-4°C	6°C

Which country is **18°C** colder than Spain?

1 mark

How much **warmer** is it in France than in Finland?

°C

1 mark

4 A school has 679 bottles of water for sports day.

They buy another 8 packs of bottled water.

Each pack contains 6 bottles.

How many bottles of water do they have in total?

Show your working

2 marks

(5) Here is a number line.

Fill each box with the correct fraction. Give each fraction in its simplest form.

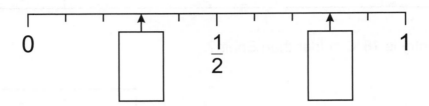

$$\frac{1}{2}$$

(6) A TV channel shows two news programmes each day.
The times that these programmes start and finish are shown below.

Find the length of each programme.

Morning News

Start 8:05 am

Finish 8:45 am

Length: [ ] minutes

Evening News

Start 9:50 pm

Finish 10:25 pm

Length: [ ] minutes

One day, the start of the morning news is delayed by **19 minutes**.
The length of the programme does not change.

What time does the morning news **finish** on this day?

7 Fill in the next two numbers in this sequence.

27,   35,   43,   51,   ☐ ,   ☐

1 mark

8 Tom buys four paint brushes.

He pays with a £5 note and gets £1.20 change.

How much does **one** paint brush cost?

Show your working

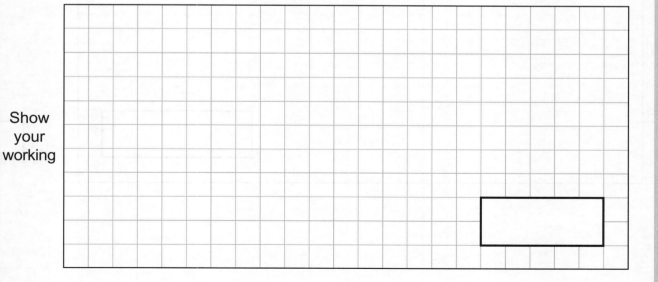

2 marks

A circle has a diameter of **22 cm**.

What is the radius of the circle?

cm

1 mark

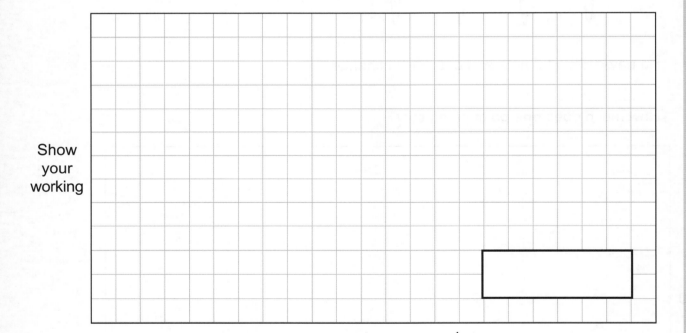 There are 16 girls and 12 boys in Holly's class.
Each class in the school has the same number of pupils.
There are **23** classes in the school.

What is the total number of pupils in Holly's school?

Show
your
working

2 marks

11 Fill in the gaps below with the prime factors of each number.

 = 28

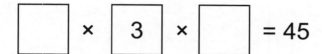 = 45

1 mark

1 mark

12 Some nets of 3D shapes are shown below.

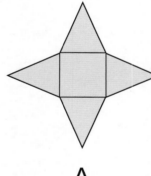

A

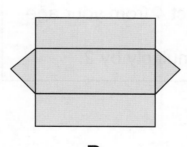

B

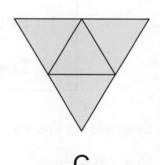

C

Give the letter of the net which could be used to make a **triangular prism**.

1 mark

13 Write **>**, **<** or **=** in each box to make the statements correct.

$$5 \times (12 - 8) \quad \boxed{} \quad 30$$

$$15 + 18 \div 3 \quad \boxed{} \quad 20$$

14 Emily follows the instructions on this card.

> 1) Subtract 4 from your age.
>
> 2) Then multiply by 2.

She gets an answer of **10**.

How old is Emily?

Show your working

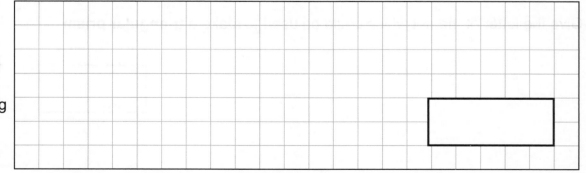

15 Find the **mean** of this set of data.

3   1   2   4   5

16 On the grid below, draw a **rectangle** that has **three times** the area of the grey triangle.

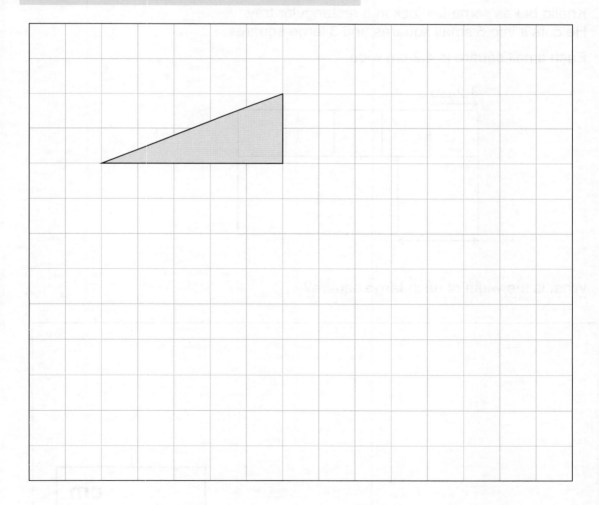

17 An isosceles triangle is shown below.

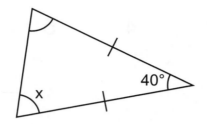

Calculate the size of angle x. Do **not** use a protractor (angle measurer).

1 mark

  18 Khalid bakes some flapjack in a rectangular tray.
He cuts it into 5 small squares and 3 large squares.

Each small square is 4.2 cm wide.

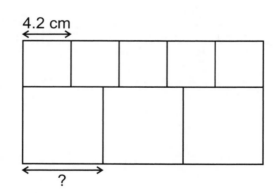

What is the width of each **large** square?

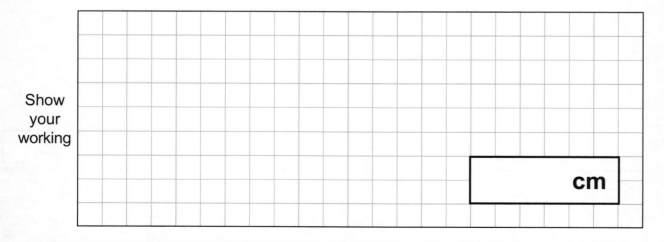

Show
your
working

cm

2 marks

19 Write the following fractions in order, from **largest** to **smallest**.

$$\frac{15}{24} \qquad \frac{9}{6} \qquad \frac{11}{8} \qquad \frac{8}{12} \qquad \frac{7}{4}$$

largest

smallest

20 A factory makes chocolate cakes.
For every **millilitre** of water in the recipe, they use 2.45 grams of flour.
One day, the factory uses **five litres** of water for the cakes.

How many grams of flour do they use?

Show your working

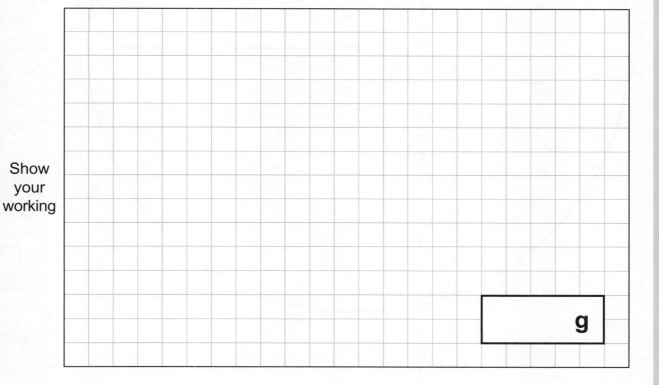

g

An ice cream van sold **90** tubs of ice cream one day.
The table shows the number of tubs of each flavour that were sold.

Flavour	Number of tubs
Vanilla	40
Chocolate	5
Strawberry	30
Toffee	15

Use this information to complete the **pie chart** below.

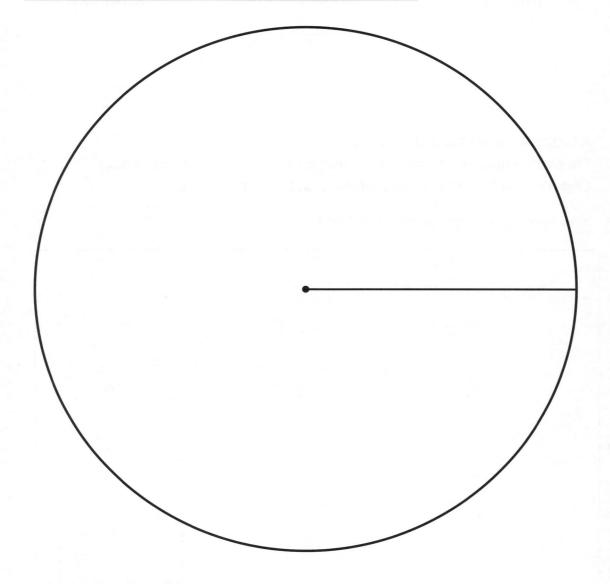

2 marks

Mathematics
Key Stage 2

Total marks

Set B
Practice Paper 1
Arithmetic

Calculator Not Allowed
30 minutes

First name	
Middle name	
Last name	
School	

Date of birth	Day		Month		Year	

(1) 565 + 7 =

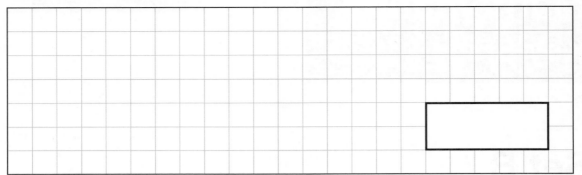

(2) 4078 − 100 =

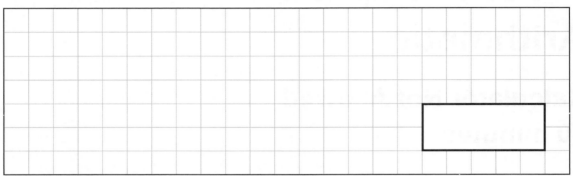

(3) 748 ÷ 1 =

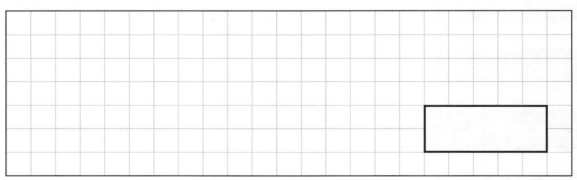

(4) 423 × 2 =

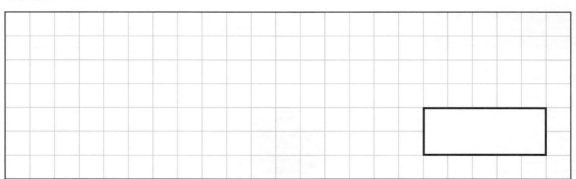

5 | ____ = 691 + 478

6 78 ÷ 6 =

7 | ____ = 721 − 20

8 5 × 6 × 9 =

(9) 29 × 4 =

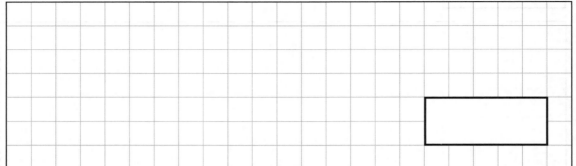

(10) 640 ÷ 8 =

(11) 283 656 + 37 529 =

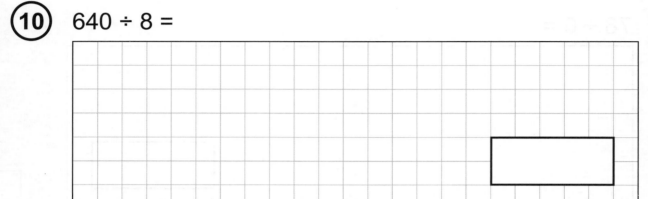

(12) 1200 × 7 =

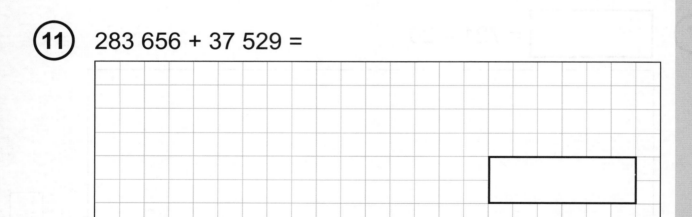

(13) 1.003 + 2.5 =

(14) 6382 × 4 =

(15) 0.39 × 100 =

16 $352 \div 4 =$

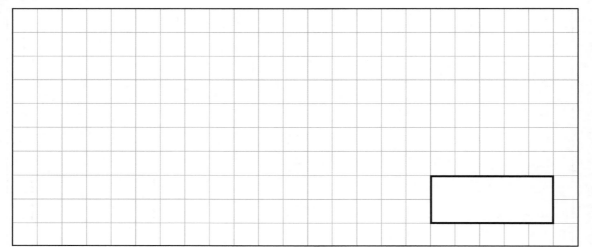

17 $136\ 428 - 28\ 999 =$

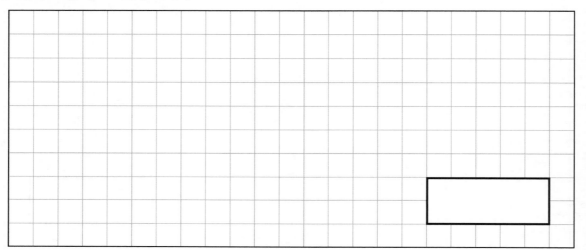

18 $184.76 - 65.62 =$

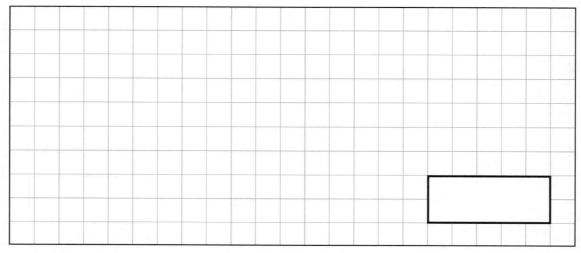

19 82 ÷ 1000 =

20 $3^3 + 4 =$

21 14 − 5.06 =

7

22 30% × 1600 =

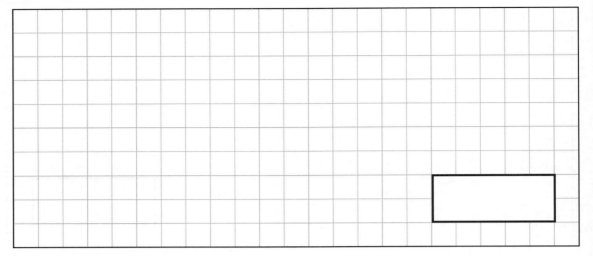

 23

$$
\begin{array}{r}
2\ 8\ 7 \\
\times\ \ 2\ 9 \\
\hline
\end{array}
$$

Show your working

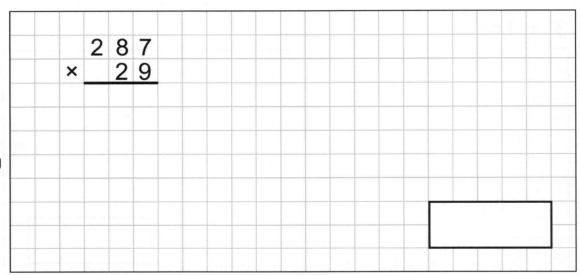

24 $\dfrac{4}{9} + \dfrac{7}{9} =$

8

25 $\dfrac{5}{14} - \dfrac{2}{7} =$

26 $38.34 \div 9 =$

27 $25 \times 2.3 =$

28   22% of 80 =

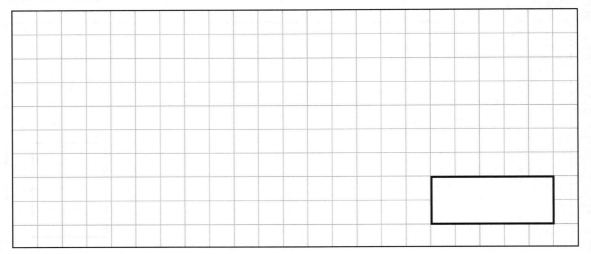

29 $\frac{4}{11} \times \frac{6}{7} =$

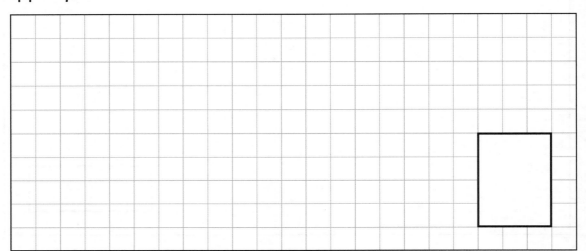

30

Show
your
working

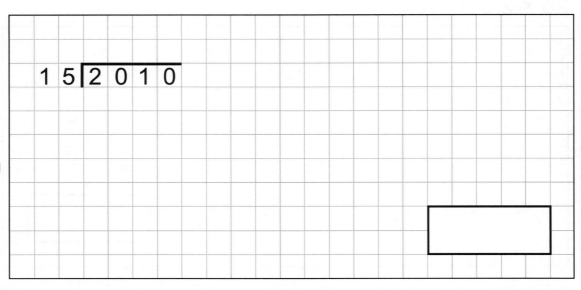

1 5 2 0 1 0

31

Show
your
working

$$\begin{array}{r} 3\ 2\ 6\ 1 \\ \times\ \ \ 8\ 3 \\ \hline \end{array}$$

2 marks

32 $\dfrac{3}{4} \div 5 =$

1 mark

33

Show
your
working

$$3\ 4\ \overline{\smash)2\ 4\ 8\ 2}$$

2 marks

(34) $\dfrac{3}{5} \times 300 =$

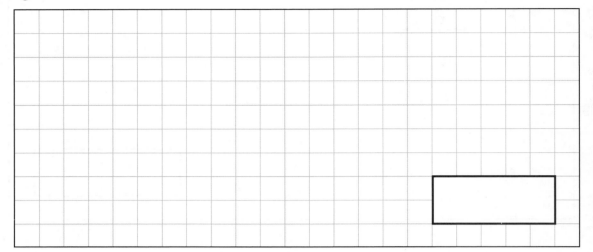

(35) $1\dfrac{2}{3} - \dfrac{4}{11} =$

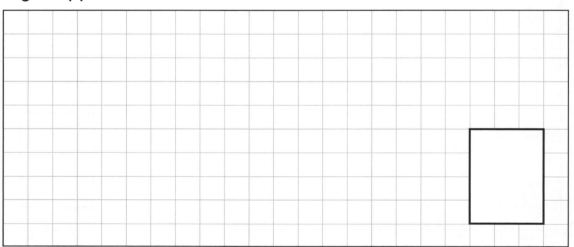

(36) $6 + 15 \div 5 - 2 =$

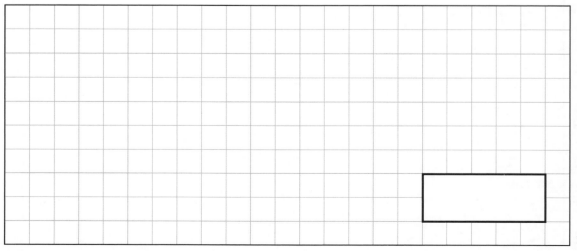

Total marks

Mathematics
Key Stage 2

Set B
Practice Paper 2
Reasoning

Calculator Not Allowed
40 minutes

First name	
Middle name	
Last name	
School	

Date of birth	Day		Month		Year	

1 A shape has vertices at (1, 1), (5, 3), (3, 5) and (5, 5).

Draw this shape on the grid below.

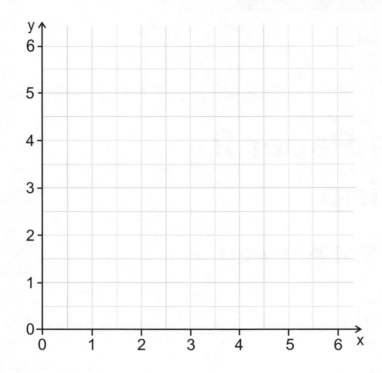

What is the name of the shape? Circle the correct answer.

Kite   Parallelogram   Rhombus

1 mark

1 mark

2 Circle the value of the **8** in **823 961**.

8000   8   800   80

80 000   800 000

3 A bag of sweets weighs 2.34 kg. Round this amount to 1 decimal place.

kg

A bag of oranges weighs 2.53 kg. Round this amount to the nearest kg.

kg

(4) How many **tenths** of this shape are shaded?

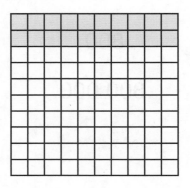

tenths

Shade another $\dfrac{3}{50}$ of the shape.

(5) Frances goes to a picnic.

At the picnic, there are **a third as many** sausage rolls as sandwiches.
There are **four times as many** scotch eggs as sausage rolls.

There are **27** sandwiches.

How many **scotch eggs** are there?

Show your working

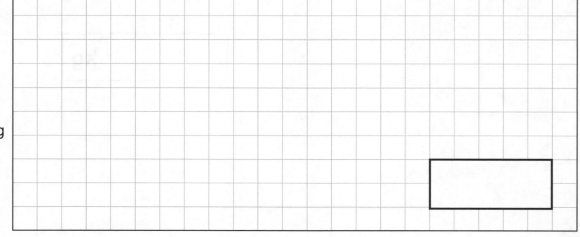

6 Circle two numbers that have a difference of **one hundredth**.

0.003   0.04   0.4   0.5

0.004   0.014   0.401

1 mark

7 Fill in the missing digits in this addition.

$$
\begin{array}{r}
2 \; \square \; 3 \; \square \\
+ \; \square \; 3 \; 9 \\
\hline
4 \; 1 \; 6 \; 0 \\
\end{array}
$$

2 marks

8 Here is a diagram of a house.

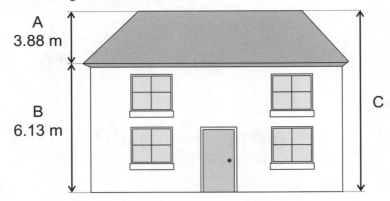

A
3.88 m

B
6.13 m

C

Find the total height (C) of the house.

| m |

The front door is **3.9 metres shorter** than part B of the house.

Work out the height of the front door.

| m |

9 Find the size of angle x in the diagram below.

Do not use a protractor (angle measurer).

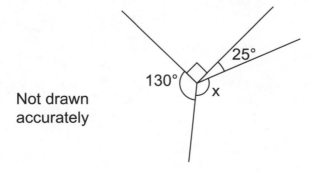

25°

130°

x

Not drawn
accurately

| ° |

Work out the value of $3^2 + 4^2$.

1 mark

Is the answer to the sum a square number?
Tick and explain your answer.

Yes ☐   No ☐

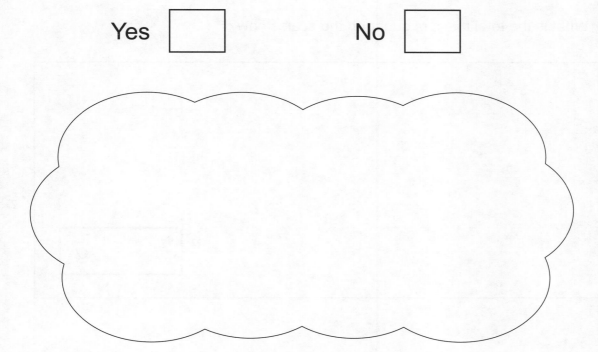

1 mark

8 identical bags of sugar are placed on some weighing scales. Their total mass is 2400 g.

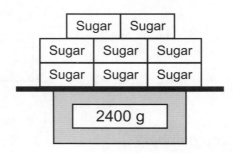

Heather takes **three** of the bags off the scales.

What is the total mass of sugar on the scales now?

Show your working

g

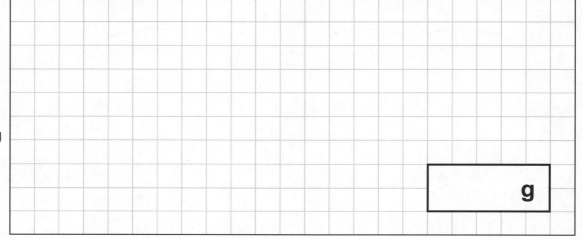

12 Millie completed a **15 mile** sponsored walk.

How many kilometres did she walk?

km

13 Stephen takes **£25.50** with him on a shopping trip.
He buys a shirt for **£13.80**.
He then spends **a third** of what he has left on his lunch.

How much money does he spend on his lunch?

Show your working

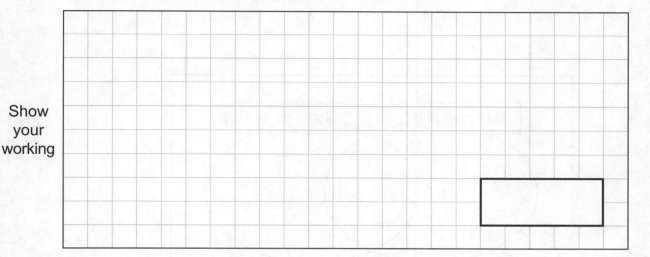

2 marks

14 Circle the amount below which is closest to 1.

0.09 $\frac{43}{50}$

85%   0.8

1 mark

15 Write each of the numbers below in the correct place on the diagram.

16   36   48

64   72

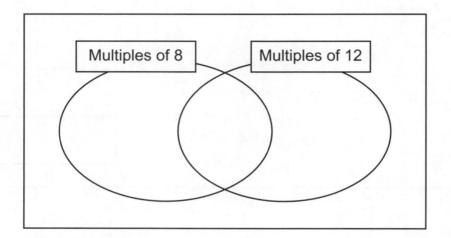

Multiples of 8   Multiples of 12

2 marks

16 Ramesh writes down a number.
He multiplies it by 3.
He divides the new number by 5, then adds 2.
The result is 3.2.

What number did he write down at the start?

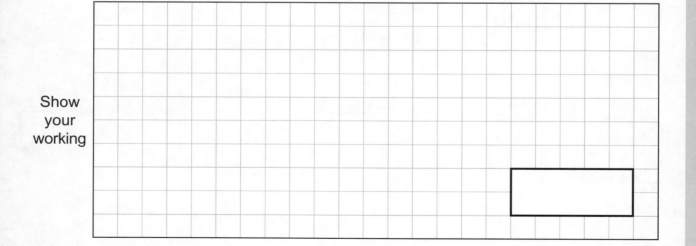

Show
your
working

2 marks

Ben has some tiles.
Each tile is the shape of a parallelogram.

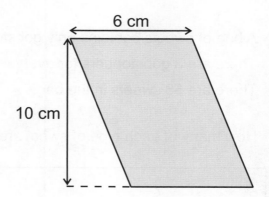

6 cm

10 cm

He places the tiles in a row to make a shape with area **720 cm²**.

How many tiles does he use?

Show
your
working

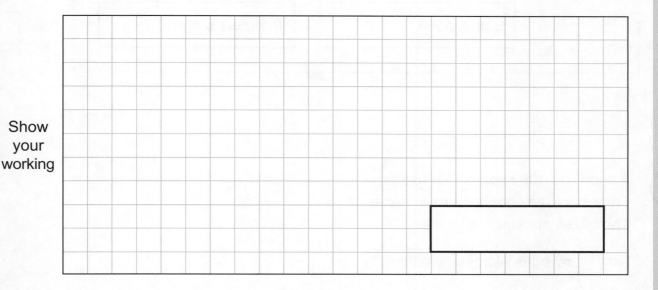

2 marks

 Emma has a piece of fabric which is $\frac{5}{7}$ metres long.
She cuts it into 3 equal pieces.

How long is each piece of fabric?

m

1 mark

19 A bag of sweets contains only gobstoppers and sherbert lemons.

There are 3 gobstoppers for every 4 sherbert lemons.

There are 56 sweets in the bag.

How many of each type of sweet are there?

Show your working

| Gobstoppers: | Sherbert lemons: |

20 A shop has 1092 spare coat hangers.

They store the coat hangers in boxes of 26.

The boxes are stacked in piles of 6.

How many **piles** of boxes are there?

Show your working

Mathematics
Key Stage 2

Total marks

Set B
Practice Paper 3
Reasoning

Calculator Not Allowed
40 minutes

First name	
Middle name	
Last name	
School	

Date of birth	Day		Month		Year	

1 Circle the **smallest** number that becomes **400** when rounded to the nearest 100.

348   401   398   449   367   450

1 mark

2 Frances runs the drink stall at her school disco.

This bar chart shows the number of drinks sold at the disco.

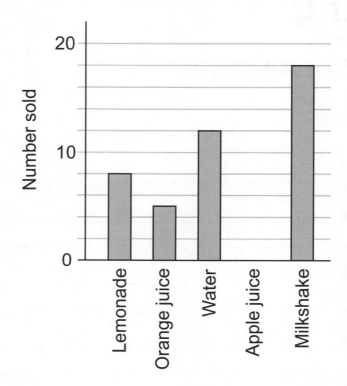

Frances sold 12 apple juice drinks.

Draw the missing bar on the chart to show this.

1 mark

How many orange juices and lemonades were sold in total?

1 mark

3 Winston says, 'When you subtract an **odd** number from another **odd** number the answer will always be **odd**.'

Is this true or false? Tick and explain your answer.

True ☐   False ☐

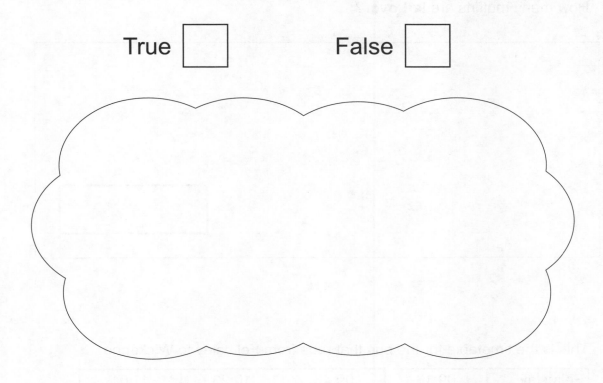

1 mark

4 Millie has a clock which shows Roman numerals. She looks at her clock and sees that the hour hand is exactly midway between **VIII** and **IX**.

What **two** times in the 24-hour clock could it be?

[   ]

1 mark

5 There are 180 muffins on sale at a school fair.

They are sold in packs of 6.

9 people each buy a pack of muffins.

How many muffins are **left over**?

Show your working

6 This is the timetable for the bus that runs from Felmsley to Wickering.

Felmsley	09:16	09:48	10:23	11:01
Bawton	09:22	09:54	10:29	11:07
Harkby	09:37	10:09	10:44	11:22
Ollerton	09:56	10:28	11:03	11:41
Wickering	10:03	10:35	11:10	11:48

How long is the bus journey from Harkby to Ollerton?

minutes

The **11:01** bus from Felmsley arrives in Wickering **14 minutes late**.

What time does it arrive in Wickering?
Give your answer using the **12-hour clock**.

(7) Here are some numbers.

0.7   0.9   0.72   0.09

Write two of these numbers in the boxes to make the calculation correct.

☐ + ☐ = 0.79

(8) List all the factors of 45.

☐

Explain why 45 isn't a prime number.

5

9 6 bottles of water cost **£3.12**.

A pot of yoghurt and **2** bottles of water cost **£1.73**.

How much does a pot of yoghurt cost?

Show your working

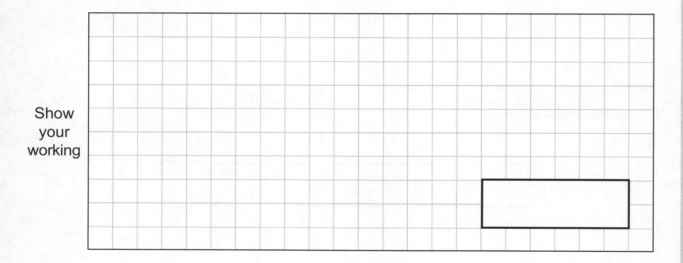

2 marks

10 Fill in the gaps to make each calculation correct.

12 × [ ] = 240

1 mark

[ ] × 30 = 1800

1 mark

11 Ruth had a tennis lesson every day for a week.
Each lesson cost the same amount, and Ruth paid **£34.65** in total.

How much did **each lesson** cost?

12 This graph shows the average monthly temperature
in a city during an eight-month period.

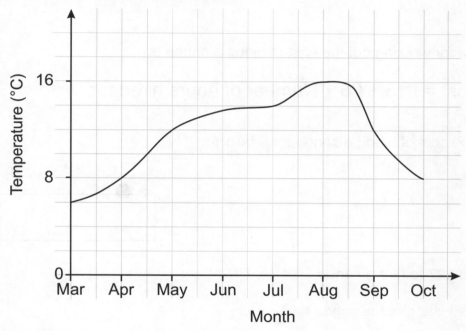

In which months was the average temperature 12 °C?

What was the difference in average temperature between April and August?

°C

(13) Find the value of ♠ and ♣ below.

6♠ = 24

♠ = [ ]

1 mark

6 + 3♣ = 75

♣ = [ ]

1 mark

(14) The formula for working out the cost of hiring a canoe is:

Cost = £15 + £6 × Number of hours hired for

Work out the cost of hiring a canoe for **4 hours**.

[ ]

1 mark

Megan paid **£27** to hire a canoe.

How long did she hire the canoe for?

Show your working

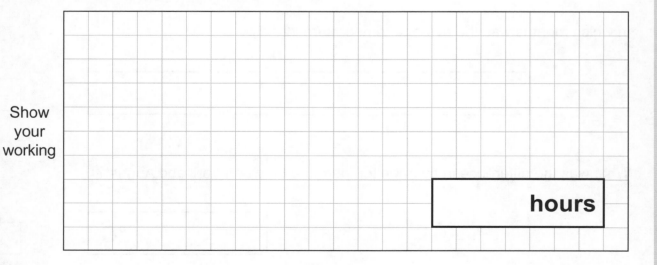

[**hours**]

2 marks

15 A square has side length 8 cm.
The square is enlarged so that it has side length 48 cm.

What is the scale factor of the enlargement?

16 Work out the size of angles g and h in the trapezium shown below.

Do **not** use a protractor (angle measurer).

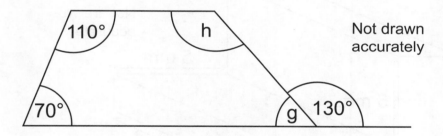

Not drawn
accurately

g = [   ] °

h = [   ] °

17 While at a theme park, Hugo spent $\frac{1}{12}$ of his time on rides and $\frac{2}{3}$ of his time queueing.

How much more of his time did Hugo spend queueing than on rides?

18 The diagram shows a shape made from two **cuboids**.

Work out the volume of the shape.

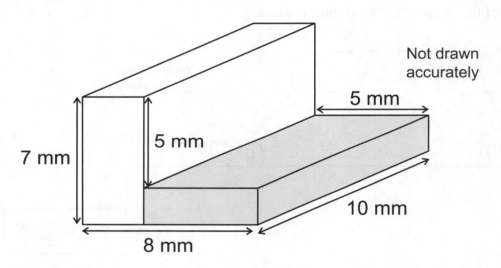

Not drawn accurately

5 mm

5 mm

7 mm

10 mm

8 mm

Show your working

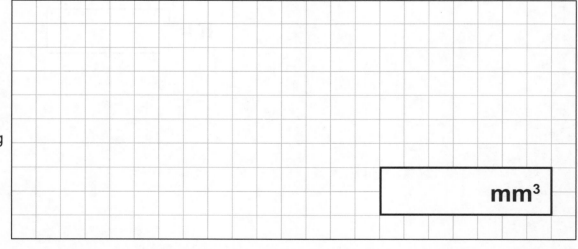

mm³

19 Padma has **120** grapes.
She keeps **35%** of them for herself.
She then shares the rest between **three** of her friends.

How many grapes does each of her friends get?

Show
your
working

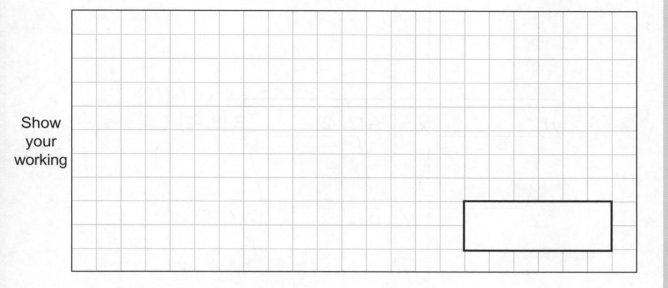

2 marks

20 Anna wants to work out the answer to **437 ÷ 23** on a calculator,
but the '2' button is broken.

Explain what she could enter into the calculator to get the right answer.

1 mark

(21) The parallelogram ABCD is shown on the axes below.

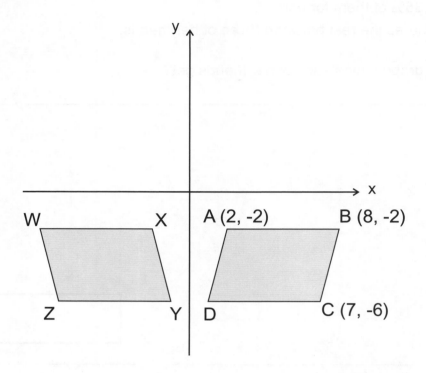

Find the coordinates of point **D**.

D = (,   )

1 mark

The shape is reflected in the y-axis to form the parallelogram WXYZ.

What are the coordinates of point **X**?

X = (,   )

1 mark

CGP

Key Stage Two

Mathematics

SATS Practice Papers
Instructions & Answer Book

Contents

Exam Set MHPP25

Practice is the best way to prepare for the KS2 Maths SATs...

...and this brilliant pack of CGP Practice Papers has been
fine-tuned to be a perfect match for the SATs in 2017 and beyond!

It contains two full sets of tests, each made up of three papers
— just like the real test pupils will take in Year 6.

We've also included full answers and mark schemes in this booklet.
That means it's easy to see which topics are their strongest, and where
they need to concentrate their revision ahead of the SATs.

Published by CGP

Editors:
Chris Corrall, Joanna Daniels, Ceara Hayden, Catherine Lear,
David Ryan, Ruth Wilbourne, Dawn Wright

Many thanks to Jonathan Wray for proofreading.
Also thanks to Jan Greenway for the copyright research.

Coin images on Set A, Paper 2, pg 3 © iStock.com

Clipart from Corel®
Printed by Elanders Ltd, Newcastle upon Tyne.

Text, design, layout and original illustrations
© Coordination Group Publications Ltd. (CGP) 2016
All rights reserved.

There are two sets of practice papers in this pack

Each **set** has:

Paper 1: Arithmetic
30 minute test
no calculators allowed   **40 marks**

Paper 2: Reasoning
40 minute test
no calculators allowed   **35 marks**

Paper 3: Reasoning
40 minute test
no calculators allowed   **35 marks**

Make sure they have these things

For all the papers:
A **pen** and a **pencil**.
A **rubber**.

For papers 2 and 3 only:
A **ruler**.
A **protractor** (angle measurer).
A **mirror**.

Doing the papers

1) The most important thing is to **understand** the questions.
Encourage them to read everything really **carefully** so they know exactly what to do.

2) Some questions will ask them to show their working.

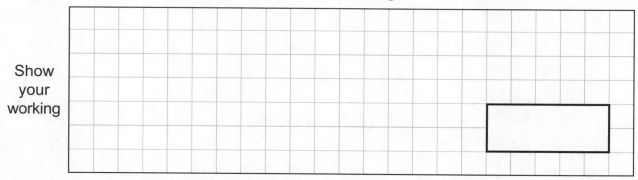

They need to do all their **working** on the **grid**, then write the **final answer** in the **box**.
Even if they get the answer **wrong**, they might get marks for trying to do the question
in the **right way**.

How to Mark the Papers

Use the answers in this booklet to mark each paper, then write the scores in the table below. For each set, add up the scores for Paper 1, Paper 2 and Paper 3 to get a **mark out of 110.**

	Paper 1 mark out of 40		**Paper 2** mark out of 35		**Paper 3** mark out of 35		**TOTAL** mark out of 110
Set A		+		+		=	
Set B		+		+		=	

The scores for these practice papers will give you a pretty good idea of whether a child is working at the **expected standard** in **Maths**.

The mark needed to achieve the **expected standard** varies from year to year, but if they get **60** or more **out of 110** then they should be on track.

Set A — Answers

Set A Paper 1

1 489
Topic tested: MULTIPLICATION — **1 mark**

2 3253
Topic tested: ADDITION — **1 mark**

3
```
  1 4 6
+   7 5
  2 2 1
  1 1
```
Topic tested: WRITTEN ADDITION — **1 mark**

4 7
Topic tested: DIVISION — **1 mark**

5 96
Topic tested: MULTIPLICATION — **1 mark**

6 357
Topic tested: SUBTRACTION — **1 mark**

7 $2 \times 3 \times 9 = 6 \times 9 = \textbf{54}$
Topic tested: MULTIPLICATION — **1 mark**

8 3
Topic tested: NEGATIVE NUMBERS — **1 mark**

9 7.1
Topic tested: SUBTRACTION — **1 mark**

10
```
  4 9 9 9 2
+   6 8 4 2
  5 6 8 3 4
  1 1 1
```
Topic tested: WRITTEN ADDITION — **1 mark**

11 3.23
Topic tested: ADDITION — **1 mark**

12 13 000
Topic tested: MULTIPLYING BY 10, 100 AND 1000 — **1 mark**

13 15 920
Topic tested: SUBTRACTION — **1 mark**

14 172.6
Topic tested: MULTIPLYING BY 10, 100 AND 1000 — **1 mark**

15
```
    9 1 7
×       6
  5 5 0 2
  1 4
```
Topic tested: WRITTEN MULTIPLICATION — **1 mark**

16 $\frac{8}{13} - \frac{5}{13} = \frac{8-5}{13} = \frac{3}{13}$
Topic tested: ADDING AND SUBTRACTING FRACTIONS — **1 mark**

17
```
  3 8⁷4 6 7
-   4 6 2 3
  3 3 8 4 4
```
Topic tested: WRITTEN SUBTRACTION — **1 mark**

18
```
  1 9.0 0 6
+ 1 2.2 8 0
  3 1.2 8 6
  1
```
Topic tested: WRITTEN ADDITION — **1 mark**

19
```
    1 0 3 2
9 9 2²8 ¹8
```
Topic tested: WRITTEN DIVISION — **1 mark**

20 0.03
Topic tested: DIVIDING BY 10, 100, AND 1000 — **1 mark**

21 $5^2 - 3^2 = 25 - 9 = \textbf{16}$
Topic tested: SQUARE AND CUBE NUMBERS — **1 mark**

22 $108 \div 12 = 9$
So $1080 \div 12 = 9 \times 10 = \textbf{90}$
Topic tested: DIVISION — **1 mark**

23 $10\% \times 400 = 400 \div 10 = 40$
$30\% \times 400 = 3 \times 40 = \textbf{120}$
Topic tested: PERCENTAGE PROBLEMS — **1 mark**

24 $\frac{4}{5} \times 125 = \frac{4 \times 125}{5} = \frac{500}{5} = \textbf{100}$
Topic tested: MULTIPLYING FRACTIONS — **1 mark**

25
```
      8 5
×     2 8
    6 8 0
      4
  1 7 0 0
  2 3 8 0
  1
```
(2 marks for the correct answer, otherwise 1 mark for the correct method with no more than one error. Award no marks if the error is the placing of digits in incorrect columns.)
Topic tested: WRITTEN MULTIPLICATION — **2 marks**

26
```
  ¹2 ²2 ⁵6 ¹0
-     4.6 7
  1 7.9 3
```
Topic tested: WRITTEN SUBTRACTION — **1 mark**

27
```
        3 4 3
14 4 8 0 2
  - 4 2
      6 0
    - 5 6
        4 2
      - 4 2
          0
```
(2 marks for the correct answer, otherwise 1 mark for a correct method with no more than one error.)
Topic tested: WRITTEN DIVISION — **2 marks**

28 $7 \times (37 - 29) = 7 \times 8 = \textbf{56}$
Topic tested: ORDER OF OPERATIONS — **1 mark**

29
```
    3 4 6
×       8
  2 7 6 8
  3 4
```
So $0.8 \times 346 = 2768 \div 10 = \textbf{276.8}$
Topic tested: WRITTEN MULTIPLICATION — **1 mark**

30 10% of 110 = 110 ÷ 10 = 11
1% of 110 = 11 ÷ 10 = 1.1
40% of 110 = 4 × 11 = 44
41% = 44 + 1.1 = **45.1**
Topic tested: PERCENTAGE PROBLEMS — **1 mark**

31 $\frac{3}{5} + \frac{7}{15} = \frac{9}{15} + \frac{7}{15} = \frac{16}{15}$ or $1\frac{1}{15}$
Topic tested: ADDING AND SUBTRACTING FRACTIONS — **1 mark**

Set A — Answers

32

```
        3 2 1 9
    ×       5 3
    ─────────────
    9 6 5 7
           2
1 6 0 9 5 0
        4
─────────────
1 7 0 6 0 7
  1 1   1 1
```

(2 marks for the correct answer, otherwise 1 mark for the correct method with no more than one error. Award no marks if the error is the placing of digits in incorrect columns.)
Topic tested: WRITTEN MULTIPLICATION

2 marks

33 $\frac{6}{7} \div 3 = \frac{6}{7 \times 3} = \frac{6}{21}$ or $\frac{2}{7}$

Topic tested: DIVIDING FRACTIONS

1 mark

34

```
        6 4
32 ) 2 0 4 8
   − 1 9 2
   ─────────
       1 2 8
     − 1 2 8
     ─────────
           0
```

(2 marks for the correct answer, otherwise 1 mark for a correct method with no more than one error.)
Topic tested: WRITTEN DIVISION

2 marks

35 $1\frac{1}{4} + \frac{4}{5} = \frac{5}{4} + \frac{4}{5} = \frac{25}{20} + \frac{16}{20} = \frac{25 + 16}{20} = \frac{41}{20}$ or $2\frac{1}{20}$

Topic tested: ADDING AND SUBTRACTING FRACTIONS

1 mark

36 $1\frac{2}{7} \times 28 = (1 \times 28) + (\frac{2}{7} \times 28) = 28 + \frac{56}{7} = 28 + 8 = \mathbf{36}$

Topic tested: MULTIPLYING FRACTIONS

1 mark

Set A Paper 2

1 27p, £0.72, £2.07, £2.70, £2.77
Topic tested: ORDERING NUMBERS

1 mark

2a Number of daisies = 4 × 10 = 40
Number of roses = 10 ÷ 2 = 5
40 − 5 = **35**

1 mark

2b Number of daffodils = $2 \times 10 + \frac{1}{2} \times 10 = 20 + 5 = 25$
Number of petunias = 2 × 10 = 20
Total number of plants = 25 + 40 + 5 + 20 = **90**
Topic tested: PICTOGRAMS

1 mark

3 10 cm³
Topic tested: VOLUME

1 mark

4 Clare's toy costs £2 + 50p + 5p + 2p + 2p = £2.59
Total cost of Clare and Hannah's toys:

```
      1 . 2 5
    + 2 . 5 9
    ─────────
      3 . 8 4
            1
```

```
    6 . 0 0
    5 9 1
    − 3 . 8 4
    ─────────
      2 . 1 6
```
so cost of James's toy = **£2.16**
(2 marks for the correct answer, otherwise 1 mark for a correct method.)
Topic tested: CALCULATIONS WITH MONEY

2 marks

5a 2
5b 110° (allow answers between 108° and 112°.)
Topics tested: 2D SHAPES & ANGLES

1 mark
1 mark

6a $4\frac{3}{7} = \frac{4 \times 7}{7} + \frac{3}{7} = \frac{28 + 3}{7} = \frac{31}{7}$

1 mark

6b 41 ÷ 6 = 6 r 5
so $\frac{41}{6} = 6\frac{5}{6}$
Topic tested: MIXED NUMBERS AND IMPROPER FRACTIONS

1 mark

7a Holly and Winston
7b 137.2 − 135.6 = **1.6 seconds**
7c 122.0 ÷ 60 = 2 r 2 = **2 minutes and 2 seconds**
Topics tested: TABLES & TIME

1 mark
1 mark
1 mark

8

```
        1 3 2
    ×     4 3
    ─────────
        3 9 6
      5 2 8 0
    ─────────
      5 6 7 6
```

(2 marks for both digits correct, otherwise 1 mark for one digit correct.)
Topic tested: WRITTEN MULTIPLICATION

2 marks

9 2 × 60 = 120 (or 60 × 2 = 120)
Topic tested: ESTIMATION AND ACCURACY

1 mark

10 $0.66 = \mathbf{66\%} = \frac{66}{100} = \frac{33}{50}$
(1 mark for each correct number.)
Topics tested: PERCENTAGES & EQUIVALENT FRACTIONS

2 marks

11 Two coffees cost

```
      1 . 9 0
    ×       2
    ─────────
      3 . 8 0
            1
```

Cost of sandwiches =

```
      8 . 8 0
    − 3 . 8 0
    ─────────
      5 . 0 0
```

£1.25 × 4 = £5.00 so they bought **4** sandwiches
(2 marks for the correct answer, otherwise 1 mark for a correct method.)
Topic tested: CALCULATIONS WITH MONEY

2 marks

Set A — Answers

12

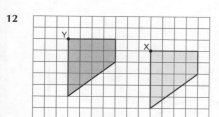

(2 marks for the complete shape translated correctly.
Otherwise, 1 mark for two vertices translated correctly.)
Topic tested: TRANSLATION
2 marks

13 E.g. 22 × 37 is 37 less than 23 × 37,
so it's 37 less than 851.
Topic tested: MULTIPLICATION
1 mark

14 Area of grey parts = area of rectangle – area of white part
Area of rectangle = 3 m × 2 m = 6 m²
Area of white part = 2 m × 2 m = 4 m²
Area of grey parts = 6 m² – 4 m² = **2 m²**
(2 marks for the correct answer, otherwise
1 mark for a correct method.)
Topic tested: AREAS
2 marks

15 Any one of 5 possible pairs:
1 and 2, 1 and 3, 2 and 4, 2 and 6, or 4 and 8
Topic tested: FACTORS
1 mark

16 Three and a half hours = 3 × 60 + 30 minutes
= 180 + 30 minutes = 210 minutes

$$\begin{array}{r} 1\ 3\ r\ 2 \\ 16\overline{)2\ 1\ 0} \\ \underline{-1\ 6} \\ 5\ 0 \\ \underline{-4\ 8} \\ 2 \end{array}$$

So she could decorate **13** complete cakes.
(2 marks for the correct answer,
otherwise 1 mark for a correct method.)
Topic tested: WRITTEN DIVISION
2 marks

17 6 + ● × ♥ = 24, so ● × ♥ = 24 – 6 = 18.
So the answers are factor pairs of 18 (not including 6,
because the three symbols represent different numbers).
● = 1, ♥ = 18 or ● = 18, ♥ = 1
● = 2, ♥ = 9 or ● = 9, ♥ = 2
Topic tested: FINDING MISSING NUMBERS
1 mark
1 mark

18 500 × 2000 = 1 000 000
So 1 000 000 ÷ 500 = **2000**
Topic tested: DIVISION
1 mark

19 If he had cycled the same distance on both days,
he would have cycled 38 + 12 = 50 km in total.
So he cycled 50 ÷ 2 = **25 km** on Saturday
Topic tested: NUMBER PROBLEMS
1 mark

20 10% of 90 = 90 ÷ 10 = 9
So Tom sold 60% of 90 = 9 × 6 = 54 cookies
Scott sold $150 \times \frac{2}{3} = \frac{150 \times 2}{3} = \frac{300}{3} = 100$ cookies

Total number of cookies sold:
$$\begin{array}{r} 5\ 4 \\ 1\ 0\ 0 \\ +\ \ \ 4\ 6 \\ \hline 2\ 0\ 0 \end{array}$$

So Dawn sold $\frac{46}{200} = \frac{23}{100} = \mathbf{23\%}$
3 marks

(3 marks for the correct answer. Otherwise, 2 marks for a
correct method with no more than one error, or 1 mark for
calculating the number of cookies sold by Tom or Scott.)
Topics tested: FRACTIONS & PERCENTAGES

Set A Paper 3

1a 75 238 — **1 mark**
1b 486 214 — **1 mark**
Topic tested: NUMBERS

2

Topic tested: SYMMETRY — **1 mark**

3a Canada (14°C – 18°C = -4°C) — **1 mark**
3b 14 °C (-8°C + 14°C = 6°C) — **1 mark**
Topic tested: NEGATIVE NUMBERS

4 They buy 8 × 6 = 48 bottles of water, so in total they have:
$$\begin{array}{r} 6\ 7\ 9 \\ +\ \ \ 4\ 8 \\ \hline 7\ 2\ 7 \end{array}$$ **bottles**
(2 marks for the correct answer, otherwise
1 mark for a correct method.)
Topics tested: MULTIPLICATION & WRITTEN ADDITION
2 marks

5 $\frac{3}{10}$ and $\frac{8}{10} = \frac{4}{5}$
(1 mark for each correct fraction.)
Topic tested: FRACTIONS
2 marks

6a Morning News: **40 minutes** — **1 mark**
Evening News: **35 minutes** — **1 mark**
6b The morning news finishes 19 minutes after 8:45 am.
19 minutes = 15 minutes + 4 minutes.
15 minutes after 8:45 am is 9 am, and 4 minutes
after 9 am is **9:04 am** (or **4 minutes past 9**).
Topic tested: TIME
1 mark

7 59, 67
Topic tested: NUMBER SEQUENCES
1 mark

8
$$\begin{array}{r} {}^4 5 .\ {}^1 0\ 0 \\ -\ \ 1 . 2\ 0 \\ \hline 3 . 8\ 0 \end{array}$$
One paintbrush = £3.80 ÷ 4
$$\begin{array}{r} 9\ 5 \\ 4\overline{)3\ 8\ ^2 0} \end{array}$$
380 is 100 times bigger than 3.80,
so divide by 100 to get the answer.
95 ÷ 100 = **£0.95** (or **95p**)
(2 marks for the correct answer, otherwise
1 mark for a correct method.)
Topic tested: CALCULATIONS WITH MONEY
2 marks

9 22 ÷ 2 = **11 cm**
Topic tested: 2D SHAPES
1 mark

10 16 + 12 = 28
$$\begin{array}{r} 2\ 8 \\ \times\ 2\ 3 \\ \hline 8\ 4 \\ 5\ 6\ 0 \\ \hline 6\ 4\ 4 \end{array}$$ **pupils**
(2 marks for the correct answer, otherwise 1 mark for a
correct method with no more than one error. No marks
if the error is the placing of digits in incorrect columns.)
Topic tested: WRITTEN MULTIPLICATION
2 marks

11a 2 × **2** × 7 (or 2 × 7 × 2) — **1 mark**
11b 3 × 3 × **5** (or 5 × 3 × 3) — **1 mark**
Topic tested: PRIME FACTORS

8

Set A — Answers

12 B
Topic tested: SHAPE NETS

1 mark

13a $5 \times (12 - 8) = 5 \times 4 = 20 < 30$

1 mark

13b $15 + 18 \div 3 = 15 + 6 = 21 > 20$
Topic tested: ORDER OF OPERATIONS

1 mark

14 Emily's age = $(10 \div 2) + 4 = 5 + 4 = \mathbf{9}$
(2 marks for the correct answer,
otherwise 1 mark for a correct method.)
Topic tested: NUMBER PROBLEMS

2 marks

15 Mean = $(3 + 1 + 2 + 4 + 5) \div 5 = 15 \div 5 = \mathbf{3}$
Topic tested: THE MEAN

1 mark

16 Area of triangle = $0.5 \times 5 \times 2 = 5$ units squared.
So a correct answer is any rectangle with an area of
$3 \times 5 = \mathbf{15}$ **units squared**. This could either be a 3×5 or
1×15 rectangle.
Topic tested: PERIMETERS & AREAS

1 mark

17 Angles in a triangle add up to 180°, so the total
of the two unknown angles is $180° - 40° = 140°$.
The two unknown angles are equal, as it's an
isosceles triangle, so x = $140° \div 2 = \mathbf{70°}$.
Topic tested: 2D SHAPES

1 mark

18 Total width of tray = $4.2 \times 5 = 21$ cm
Width of large square = $21 \div 3 = \mathbf{7\ cm}$
(2 marks for the correct answer, otherwise
1 mark for a correct method.)
Topic tested: NUMBER PROBLEMS

2 marks

19 Write each fraction with denominator 24:
$$\frac{15}{24}, \frac{9}{6} = \frac{36}{24}, \frac{11}{8} = \frac{33}{24}, \frac{8}{12} = \frac{16}{24}, \frac{7}{4} = \frac{42}{24}$$
In order from largest to smallest:
$$\mathbf{\frac{7}{4}, \frac{9}{6}, \frac{11}{8}, \frac{8}{12}, \frac{15}{24}}$$
Topic tested: COMPARING FRACTIONS

1 mark

20 Five litres = 5000 ml, so they use
5000×2.45 g $= 5 \times 1000 \times 2.45$ g $= 5 \times 2450$ g =

$$\begin{array}{r} 2\ 4\ 5\ 0 \\ \times \qquad\quad 5 \\ \hline 1\ \underset{2}{2}\ \underset{2}{2}\ 5\ 0\ g \end{array}$$

(2 marks for the correct answer, otherwise
1 mark for using a correct method.)
Topics tested: CONVERSIONS & WRITTEN MULTIPLICATION

2 marks

21 $360° \div 90 = 4°$ per tub
Vanilla angle: $40 \times 4° = 160°$
Chocolate angle: $5 \times 4° = 20°$
Strawberry angle: $30 \times 4° = 120°$
Toffee angle: $15 \times 4° = 60°$
E.g.

(2 marks for correct angles and labels on the pie
chart, otherwise 1 mark for any two sectors with
the correct angle and correctly labelled.)
Topic tested: PIE CHARTS

2 marks

Set B — Answers

Set B Paper 1

1 572
Topic tested: ADDITION — **1 mark**

2 3978
Topic tested: SUBTRACTION — **1 mark**

3 748
Topic tested: DIVISION — **1 mark**

4 846
Topic tested: MULTIPLICATION — **1 mark**

5
```
    6 9 1
  + 4 7 8
  ───────
  1 1 6 9
      1
```
Topic tested: WRITTEN ADDITION — **1 mark**

6
```
    1 3
  6│7 ¹8
```
Topic tested: WRITTEN DIVISION — **1 mark**

7 701
Topic tested: SUBTRACTION — **1 mark**

8 5 × 6 × 9 = 30 × 9 = **270**
Topic tested: MULTIPLICATION — **1 mark**

9
```
    2 9
  ×   4
  ─────
  1 1 6
    3
```
Topic tested: WRITTEN MULTIPLICATION — **1 mark**

10 64 ÷ 8 = 8, so
640 ÷ 8 = 8 × 10 = **80**
Topic tested: DIVISION — **1 mark**

11
```
  2 8 3 6 5 6
+   3 7 5 2 9
─────────────
  3 2 1 1 8 5
  1 1 1   1
```
Topic tested: WRITTEN ADDITION — **1 mark**

12 12 × 7 = 84 so,
1200 × 7 = 84 × 100 = **8400**
Topic tested: MULTIPLICATION — **1 mark**

13 3.503
Topic tested: ADDITION — **1 mark**

14
```
    6 3 8 2
  ×       4
  ─────────
  2 5 5 2 8
    1 3
```
Topic tested: WRITTEN MULTIPLICATION — **1 mark**

15 39
Topic tested: MULTIPLYING BY 10, 100 AND 1000 — **1 mark**

16
```
      8 8
  4│3 5 ³2
```
Topic tested: WRITTEN DIVISION — **1 mark**

17
```
1 ²3 ¹5⁶ ¹3⁴ ¹2 ⁱ8
−     2 8 9 9 9
───────────────
1 0 7 4 2 9
```
Topic tested: WRITTEN SUBTRACTION — **1 mark**

18
```
  1 ⁷8 ¹4 . 7 6
−   6 5 . 6 2
─────────────
  1 1 9 . 1 4
```
Topic tested: WRITTEN SUBTRACTION — **1 mark**

19 0.082
Topic tested: DIVIDING BY 10, 100 AND 1000 — **1 mark**

20 $3^3 + 4 = 27 + 4 =$ **31**
Topic tested: SQUARE AND CUBE NUMBERS — **1 mark**

21
```
  ₓ¹3₄ . ¹⁹0 ¹0
−     5 . 0 6
─────────────
      8 . 9 4
```
Topic tested: WRITTEN SUBTRACTION — **1 mark**

22 10% × 1600 = 1600 ÷ 10 = 160
30% × 1600 = 160 × 3 = **480**
Topic tested: PERCENTAGE PROBLEMS — **1 mark**

23
```
      2 8 7
  ×     2 9
  ─────────
  2 5 8 3
    7 7
  5 7 4 0
  1 1
  8 3 2 3
  1   1
```
(2 marks for the correct answer, otherwise 1 mark for the correct method with no more than one error. Award no marks if the error is the placing of digits in incorrect columns.)
Topic tested: WRITTEN MULTIPLICATION — **2 marks**

24 $\frac{4}{9}+\frac{7}{9}=\frac{4+7}{9}=\frac{11}{9}$ or $1\frac{2}{9}$
Topic tested: ADDING AND SUBTRACTING FRACTIONS — **1 mark**

25 $\frac{5}{14}-\frac{2}{7}=\frac{5}{14}-\frac{4}{14}=\frac{5-4}{14}=\frac{1}{14}$
Topic tested: ADDING AND SUBTRACTING FRACTIONS — **1 mark**

26
```
      4 2 6
  9│3 8 ²3 ⁵4
```
So 38.34 ÷ 9 = 426 ÷ 100 = **4.26**
Topic tested: WRITTEN DIVISION — **1 mark**

27 20 × 2.3 = 2 × (10 × 2.3) = 2 × 23 = 46
5 × 2.3 = (10 × 2.3) ÷ 2 = 23 ÷ 2 = 11.5
So 25 × 2.3 = 46 + 11.5 = **57.5**
Topic tested: MULTIPLICATION — **1 mark**

28 10% of 80 = 80 ÷ 10 = 8
20% of 80 = 8 × 2 = 16
2% of 80 = 16 ÷ 10 = 1.6
22% of 80 = 16 + 1.6 = **17.6**
Topic tested: PERCENTAGE PROBLEMS — **1 mark**

29 $\frac{4}{11}\times\frac{6}{7}=\frac{4\times6}{11\times7}=\frac{24}{77}$
Topic tested: MULTIPLYING FRACTIONS — **1 mark**

30
```
        1 3 4
  15│2 0 1 0
   − 1 5
     ─────
       5 1
     − 4 5
       ─────
         6 0
       − 6 0
         ───
           0
```
(2 marks for the correct answer, otherwise 1 mark for a correct method with no more than one error.)
Topic tested: WRITTEN DIVISION — **2 marks**

Set B — Answers

31

```
      3 2 6 1
   ×      8 3
   _____
      9 7 8 3
            1
   2 6 0 8 8 0
     2 4
   _____
   2 7 0 6 6 3
   1 1 1
```

(2 marks for the correct answer, otherwise 1 mark for the correct method with no more than one error. Award no marks if the error is the placing of digits in incorrect columns.)
Topic tested: WRITTEN MULTIPLICATION

2 marks

32 $\dfrac{3}{4} \div 5 = \dfrac{3}{4 \times 5} = \dfrac{3}{20}$
Topic tested: DIVIDING FRACTIONS

1 mark

33

```
           7 3
   34 ) 2 4 8 2
      - 2 3 8
      _____
          1 0 2
        - 1 0 2
        _____
              0
```

(2 marks for the correct answer, otherwise 1 mark for a correct method with no more than one error.)
Topic tested: WRITTEN DIVISION

2 marks

34 $\dfrac{3}{5} \times 300 = \dfrac{3 \times 300}{5} = \dfrac{900}{5} = \mathbf{180}$
Topic tested: MULTIPLYING FRACTIONS

1 mark

35 $1\dfrac{2}{3} - \dfrac{4}{11} = \dfrac{5}{3} - \dfrac{4}{11} = \dfrac{55}{33} - \dfrac{12}{33} = \dfrac{43}{33}$ or $1\dfrac{10}{33}$
Topic tested: ADDING AND SUBTRACTING FRACTIONS

1 mark

36 $6 + 15 \div 5 - 2 = 6 + 3 - 2 = \mathbf{7}$
Topic tested: ORDER OF OPERATIONS

1 mark

Set B Paper 2

1a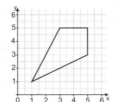

1b Kite
Topics tested: COORDINATES & 2D SHAPES

1 mark

2 800 000
Topic tested: NUMBERS

1 mark

3a 2.3 kg
3b 3 kg
Topic tested: ROUNDING

1 mark
1 mark

4a 20 of the 100 squares are shaded: $\dfrac{20}{100} = \dfrac{2}{10} = \mathbf{2\ tenths}$
4b $\dfrac{3}{50} = \dfrac{6}{100}$ so **6** more squares should be shaded.
Topic tested: EQUIVALENT FRACTIONS

1 mark
1 mark

5 There are $\dfrac{1}{3} \times 27 = 9$ sausage rolls,
so there are $4 \times 9 = \mathbf{36}$ scotch eggs.
(2 marks for the correct answer, otherwise 1 mark for a correct method.)
Topic tested: NUMBER PROBLEMS

2 marks

6 0.014 and 0.004
Topic tested: DECIMALS

1 mark

7

```
   2 8 3 1
 + 1 3 2 9
 _____
   4 1 6 0
```

(2 marks for four digits correct, otherwise 1 mark for three digits correct.)
Topic tested: WRITTEN ADDITION

2 marks

8a

```
   3 . 8 8
 + 6 . 1 3
 _____
 1 0 . 0 1  m
   1   1
```

1 mark

8b

```
   5
   6 . 1 3
 - 3 . 9 0
 _____
   2 . 2 3  m
```

Topics tested: WRITTEN ADDITION & WRITTEN SUBTRACTION

1 mark

9 Angles around a point add up to 360°, so:
x = 360° – 130° – 90° – 25° = **115°**
Topic tested: ANGLES

1 mark

10a $3^2 + 4^2 = 9 + 16 = \mathbf{25}$
10b Yes, because $5^2 = 25$.
Topic tested: SQUARE NUMBERS

1 mark
1 mark

11 1 bag of sugar weighs 2400 g ÷ 8 = 300 g
3 bags weigh 3 × 300 g = 900 g
2400 g – 900 g = **1500 g**
(2 marks for the correct answer, otherwise 1 mark for a correct method.)
Topic tested: NUMBER PROBLEMS

2 marks

12 5 miles ≈ 8 km. (15 ÷ 5) × 8 = 3 × 8 = **24 km**
Topic tested: UNIT CONVERSIONS

1 mark

Set B — Answers

Set B Paper 3

13 Money left after buying shirt:

$$
\begin{array}{r}
2\,{}^{4}\!5\,.\,{}^{1}5\;0 \\
-\;1\;3\,.\,8\;0 \\
\hline
1\;1\,.\,7\;0
\end{array}
$$

Cost of lunch = £11.70 ÷ 3

$$
\begin{array}{r}
3\;9\;0 \\
3\,\overline{)1\;1\,{}^{2}7\;0}
\end{array}
$$

1170 is 100 times bigger than 11.70, so divide by 100 to get the answer.
390 ÷ 100 = **£3.90**
(2 marks for the correct answer, otherwise 1 mark for a correct method.)
Topic tested: CALCULATIONS WITH MONEY

2 marks

14 As decimals the numbers are:
0.09, $\dfrac{43}{50} = \dfrac{86}{100} = 0.86$, $85\% = 0.85$, 0.8
So $\dfrac{43}{50}$ is closest to 1.
Topic tested: FRACTIONS, DECIMALS AND PERCENTAGES

1 mark

15

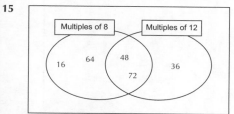

(2 marks for all numbers in the correct areas of the diagram, otherwise 1 mark for three numbers in the correct areas.)
Topic tested: MULTIPLES

2 marks

16 $3.2 - 2 = 1.2$
$1.2 \times 5 = 6$
$6 \div 3 = \mathbf{2}$
(2 marks for the correct answer, otherwise 1 mark for a correct method.)
Topic tested: NUMBER PROBLEMS

2 marks

17 1 tile has area 6 cm × 10 cm = 60 cm²
$720 \div 60 = 72 \div 6 = \mathbf{12}$ tiles
(2 marks for the correct answer, otherwise 1 mark for a correct method.)
Topic tested: AREAS

2 marks

18 $\dfrac{5}{7} \div 3 = \dfrac{5}{7 \times 3} = \dfrac{\mathbf{5}}{\mathbf{21}}$ **m**
Topic tested: DIVIDING FRACTIONS

1 mark

19 There are 3 + 4 = 7 shares in total.
1 share is 56 ÷ 7 = 8 sweets.
So there are 3 × 8 = **24** gobstoppers.
and 4 × 8 = **32** sherbert lemons
(2 marks for both correct answers, otherwise 1 mark for working out the number of sweets in one share.)
Topic tested: RATIO AND PROPORTION

2 marks

20 Number of boxes of coat hangers:

$$
\begin{array}{r}
4\;2 \\
26\,\overline{)1\;0\;9\;2} \\
-\,1\;0\;4 \\
\hline
5\;2 \\
-\;5\;2 \\
\hline
0
\end{array}
$$

Number of piles = 42 ÷ 6 = **7**
(3 marks for the correct answer. Otherwise, 2 marks for finding 42 or for a correct method with no more than one error. 1 mark for a correct method with more than one error.)
Topic tested: WRITTEN DIVISION

3 marks

Set B Paper 3

1 367
Topic tested: ROUNDING

1 mark

2a

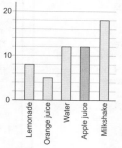

1 mark

2b $5 + 8 = \mathbf{13}$
Topic tested: BAR CHARTS

1 mark

3 False. An odd number subtracted from another odd number will always give an even number,
e.g. 17 − 5 = 12.
Topic tested: NUMBER PROBLEMS

1 mark

4 08:30 or 20:30
Topic tested: ROMAN NUMERALS

1 mark

5 $9 \times 6 = 54$

$$
\begin{array}{r}
1\;{}^{7}\!8\;{}^{1}0 \\
-\;\;\;\;5\;4 \\
\hline
1\;2\;6
\end{array}
$$
muffins
(2 marks for the correct answer, otherwise 1 mark for a correct method.)
Topics tested: MULTIPLICATION & WRITTEN SUBTRACTION

2 marks

6a 19 minutes
6b 12:02 pm
Topic tested: TIMETABLES

1 mark
1 mark

7 0.7 and 0.09
Topic tested: DECIMALS

1 mark

8a 1, 3, 5, 9, 15, 45
8b 45 has factors other than 1 and itself, so it can't be a prime number.
Topics tested: FACTORS & PRIME NUMBERS

1 mark
1 mark

9 6 bottles cost £3.12, so 2 bottles cost £3.12 ÷ 3 = £1.04
Yoghurt costs £1.73 − £1.04 = **£0.69** or **69p**
OR
1 bottle costs £3.12 ÷ 6 = £0.52
2 bottles cost £0.52 × 2 = £1.04
Yoghurt costs £1.73 − £1.04 = **£0.69** or **69p**
(2 marks for the correct answer, otherwise 1 mark for a correct method.)
Topic tested: CALCULATIONS WITH MONEY

2 marks

10a $12 \times \mathbf{20} = 240$
10b $\mathbf{60} \times 30 = 1800$
Topic tested: MULTIPLICATION

1 mark
1 mark

11

$$
\begin{array}{r}
4\;9\;5 \\
7\,\overline{)3\;4\;{}^{6}6\;{}^{3}5}
\end{array}
$$

495 ÷ 100 = 4.95, so £34.65 ÷ 7 = **£4.95**
Topic tested: WRITTEN DIVISION

1 mark

12a May and September
12b $16 - 8 = 8\ {}^{\circ}\text{C}$
Topic tested: LINE GRAPHS

1 mark
1 mark

Set B — Answers

13a	♠ = 24 ÷ 6 = **4**	**1 mark**
13b	3♣ = 75 − 6 = 69	
	♣ = 69 ÷ 3 = **23**	**1 mark**
	Topic tested: USING SYMBOLS AND LETTERS	
14a	£15 + £6 × 4 = £15 + £24 = **£39**	**1 mark**
14b	£27 = £15 + £6 × number of hours hired	
	£27 − £15 = £12 = £6 × number of hours hired	
	12 ÷ 6 = 2, so she hired the canoe for **2** hours.	**2 marks**
	(2 marks for the correct answer, otherwise	
	1 mark for a correct method.)	
	Topic tested: FORMULAS AND EXPRESSIONS	
15	48 ÷ 8 = **6**	**1 mark**
	Topic tested: SIMILAR SHAPES	
16	Angles on a straight line add up to 180° so	
	angle g = 180° − 130° = **50°**	**1 mark**
	Total of known angles in trapezium	
	= 110° + 70° + 50° = 230°	
	Angles in a quadrilateral add up to 360°,	
	so angle h = 360° − 230° = **130°**	**1 mark**
	Topics tested: ANGLE RULES & 2D SHAPES	
17	$\frac{2}{3} - \frac{1}{12} = \frac{8}{12} - \frac{1}{12} = \frac{7}{12}$	**1 mark**
	Topic tested: ADDING AND SUBTRACTING FRACTIONS	
18	Width of white cuboid = 8 mm − 5 mm = 3 mm	
	Volume of white cuboid = 7 × 3 × 10 = 210 mm³	
	Height of shaded cuboid = 7 mm − 5 mm = 2 mm	
	Volume of shaded cuboid = 2 × 5 × 10 = 100 mm³	
	Total volume = 210 + 100 = **310 mm³**	**2 marks**
	(2 marks for the correct answer, otherwise 1 mark for	
	calculating the volume of either cuboid correctly.)	
	Topic tested: VOLUME	
19	10% of 120 = 120 ÷ 10 = 12	
	30% of 120 = 12 × 3 = 36	
	5% of 120 = 12 ÷ 2 = 6	
	35% of 120 = 36 + 6 = 42	
	Remaining grapes = 120 − 42 = 78	
	$\overset{2\ \ 6}{3\overline{)7\ ^{1}8}}$, so each of her friends gets **26 grapes**.	**2 marks**
	(2 marks for the correct answer, otherwise	
	1 mark for calculating 35% of 120.)	
	Topic tested: NUMBER PROBLEMS	
20	E.g. Double both numbers in the division to get rid of the	
	digit 2: 874 ÷ 46 will give the same answer as 437 ÷ 23.	
	Or	
	Split up 23 into a pair of numbers that don't contain the	
	digit 2, such as 19 + 4, then use brackets to do the addition	
	before the division: 437 ÷ (19 + 4).	**1 mark**
	Topics tested: NUMBER PROBLEMS	
21a	Point A is 6 units to the left of point B.	
	So point D is 6 units to the left of point C.	
	The x-coordinate of point D is 7 − 6 = 1.	
	Point D has the same y-coordinate as point C.	
	So the coordinates of point D are **(1, -6)**.	**1 mark**
21b	Point X is the image of point A.	
	Point A is 2 units to the right of the y-axis, so point X is 2	
	units to the left of the y-axis. Its x-coordinate is -2.	
	Point X has the same y-coordinate as point A.	
	The coordinates of point X are **(-2, -2)**.	**1 mark**
	Topics tested: USING COORDINATES & REFLECTION	